—— THE ——
ASPECT OF
Relationships

THE
ASPECT OF
Relationships

FRANCESS SAMURA

Published by CALABASH PRINCESS LLC
First Printing, July 2023 in the United States

THE ASPECT OF RELATIONSHIPS
© Francess Samura
ISBN: 979-8-9886534-2-4

Publish by
Calabash Princess LLC
Atlanta
United States
Website: www.francesssamura.com
Email:blessed@francesssamura.com
Francess.calabash@gmail.com

Facebook: Francess Samura
Instagram: Francess.calabash

To all facing relationship challenges, this book is for you. Whether it's financial strains, shattered hearts, the loss of a beloved, family troubles, or navigating hardships, remember this: nothing endures eternally. Just as darkness surrenders to dawn and the moon yields to sunlight, so too shall your troubles pave the path for joy and fulfilment.

To my beloved, wonderful children

Abijah Samura and Benaiah Samura,

My reason for living, my inspiration and my light of hope,
I thank God for blessing me with your unconditional love.
May God always protect you from those who wish you ill.

This book will help you through your pathway in life journey.
I Love you to the moon and back.

To Alieu Iscandari Esq. Words cannot express how much I
love and appreciate you. Thank you for helping us through this
journey. May God continue to bless you and Halima Khamis.

To Mohammed Buhari. Thank you. I pray that your kindness
will continue to spread across your generation yet unborn.
God will forever water your tree of life. And may your mom's
soul rest in peace. The Late Haja Onike Sakina Buhari

My dear friend turned out to be a sister—
the Late Miss Jassie Harris.

May your soul continue to rest in peace.

For me to get to this level, you inspired me. It was your idea
for me to start reading books. " Cess, start reading books,
and it will help you in future."

Your words are still in my head. Your love for reading has taken me on this beautiful journey. Thank you, my friend and sister. I will forever miss you, Jass.

To Victor Inyang Nyong MCIPS.

This book has been to different editors without my satisfaction. However, once you touch it, I instantly know you're the best version of myself. Thank you for your patience and the ungodly hours of phone calls. I appreciate you.

Thanks to all my friends, family and social media supporters, especially my Facebook friends and followers. Thanks for all your kind words and encouragement throughout the years.

Dear Readers,

Thank you for reading "The Aspect of Relationships" - Spiritual, Personal, Friendship, and Family Relationships. This book will leave an everlasting impact on your heart and mind. The ten chapters will take you through the complexities of relationships. The deep insights and practical advice shared will help you develop a profound understanding of nurturing and strengthening relationships with your loved ones.

This book is filled with captivating chapters and will take you on a journey from the beginning to the end.

It starts with a question; Is My relationship healthy or Unhealthy? Chapter one is the introductory chapter, setting the benchmark for the remaining nine chapters.

The wisdom and insights you will gather from this book are priceless, and I guarantee that this book will take you on a self-assessment journey. Whatever your situation is, whatever you are going through now, this book will validate your thought process and feelings. Whether you've been through childhood troubles or struggling with personal day-to-day life relationship journeys, this book will be instrumental in transforming both your personal and professional life.

This book will take you on a journey with your subconscious mind and assist you in managing relationships on a daily basis as you follow the journey of James Tapia Kanu from chapter two onwards, who is the main character. His teaching skills will prove valuable for your daily routine and future endeavours in life.

So, open your heart and mind, for this book is your guide through the intricate tapestry of relationships. Let the words within its pages resonate with your soul as you embark on this remarkable journey towards cultivating meaningful and enduring connections.

Are you ready to explore the captivating world of relationships? Then brace yourself for an unforgettable odyssey within the pages of "The Aspect of Relationships."

Grab a pen and paper to jot down some goals and key points you would like to take away from this book; writing them down increases the chances of achieving them exponentially.

I hope you will enjoy reading this book as much as I enjoyed researching and writing it. It was a life-changing experience for me, and I aspire to impact your life through its contents positively. Please share your experience with me after reading it.

Thank you, and may God bless you.

Francess Samura

Contents

Chapter One

Is My Relationship Healthy or Unhealthy?

The Beautifully Chaotic Journey of Love and Connection

The word "relationship" may seem like a simple noun used daily by millions to describe their connections with friends, family, colleagues, and even their interactions with the environment. But in reality, it surrounds the most complicated and fascinating biological creations on Earth and has lasting impacts on our society. These connections create love and harmony and lay the foundation for future generations to flourish, but they destroy the blessings they were meant to nourish without proper care. Soured relationships wage wars and leave one stranded amid 'us' vs 'them,' a type of conflict that can drag on for years and, in the worst cases, end in fatality.

The symbiotic nature of relationships ensures survival, and this truth is the backbone of our world. Since the beginning of time, the first man and woman were created to have a relationship with each other and God. Without them, the world as we know it would not exist. As human beings, connecting with others is an essential part of our existence. So, how is it possible for us to be so confused and unsuccessful in that area of life? And how can we ensure that our relationships work?

We enter relationships for various reasons and fall in love with people we don't know. While it can sometimes end up great, it can also have devastating consequences. People can hurt us, and we are liable to hurt others too. However, in any relationship, if someone is not meant to be in your life journey, God will continuously allow them to hurt you until you realise your true potential and that you are strong and courageous enough to let them go, set yourself free, and discover new opportunities.

Therefore, be mindful of the people who are not meant to be in your life journey that you keep holding onto for some reason or another. Sometimes, you must let go to develop, grow, and discover yourself. If you don't let go, how will you know what awaits you on the other side? Embrace the beautiful complexity of relationships, nurture love and community, and allow yourself to flourish.

In any relationship, understanding your desires from the start is crucial, as knowing the WHY and with WHOM is essential for a healthy relationship to blossom. However, knowing yourself, your spiritual and mental wellness, the universal truth, your environment, and most importantly, your supernatural self is essential before embarking on any relationship. By doing so, you can adeptly love someone else wholeheartedly.

It's crucial to respect yourself and your environment by not inviting just anyone into your personal space. Your space is your sacred ground, and your body is your temple; guarding and protecting it is crucial for your well-being and comfort. Since we don't know people, even though we might think we do — some people have a whole generation following them, some have generational curses which they haven't broken, some might have spiritual husbands or wives, bad omens, and some are even killers or the big P before they met you — we must be mindful of whom we let our soul dance with. Not everyone is destined to be a part of your life journey.

Women are often vulnerable to such people, especially when they already have children; unknowingly exposing them to these individuals can be detrimental. Another aspect is during copulation, your partner is depositing all that negativity inside you when having sexual intimacy, leaving you with a sense of unease. Another common problem in our generation is we sometimes have multiple partners and invite different spirits into our souls, and we often ask ourselves why things aren't going right. Why am I having difficulties in life? Why am I having financial problems? Why am I not getting married? These are just some of the questions you may be asking yourself. The simple answer is that we're not selecting the right people in our lives or making the right choices. Trust should be earned and not given away freely.

Listening to your inner self is crucial, as your subconscious mind repeatedly reminds you of your true self. Pay attention to the signs that tell you it's not right. Nurture yourself and protect your space to create healthy, thriving relationships.

Why is the divorce rate so high in our generation?

Starting in 2019, the world faced a tumultuous time with the onset of a pandemic that uprooted people's lives in unprecedented ways. With lockdowns imposed in most parts of the planet, individuals were forced to stay home, and jobs and schools transitioned to a virtual world, leading to increased interaction within families.

While this may sound idyllic, the reality was often a challenge, with couples spending more time together and navigating difficult behavioural choices in the home environment. Trapped in each other's space due to the pandemic, conflicts of opinion emerged, causing many relationships to unravel, thus leading to a spike in divorces.

Additionally, the feeling of isolation due to the pandemic, with many reporting a lack of close friends, only exacerbated the situation.

Sadly, communication issues have become a major factor in many relationships, causing damage across generations. In some parts of the world, children are even legally allowed to divorce their parents, highlighting the severity of the problem.

Of course, every marriage wants to last forever, but sometimes divorce is the only solution. Unhealthy or abusive relationships, whether mental, financial, physical, verbal, or sexual, can lead to immense pain and suffering, sometimes even resulting in severe disabilities or death. Unfortunately, these relationships are becoming increasingly popular among our social media generation, fuelled by peer pressure and a lack of awareness about healthy relationships.

Betrayal is another major problem in our generation. Some people take cheating as casual nowadays and invent different names for it. Some refer to it as swindlers, freeloaders, open marriages, and more. On the other hand, some people are serial cyber cheaters in relationships and don't consider it as such.

There are so many forms of betrayal that can impact marriages, and I will name a few — for example, not sticking up for your partner, jealousy, hurt, rivalry, lying, using your partner's past against them, disrespecting your partner in public, and keeping secrets from your partner.

Body image and material satisfaction are other factors in the high divorce rate. How people evaluate themselves plays a major role in society today. Many of us, at some point in our lives, experience negative body image or negative body shaming from someone.

It is tough to feel beautiful and sexy when we are bombarded daily with altered and unrealistic images of different body types on social media and in our environment. Sometimes, it can even be our partners who are body-shaming us and hurting our self-esteem. Lack of self-confidence and poor body image can profoundly affect our relationships.

Despite these challenges, it's important to remember that healthy relationships are possible, and seeking help and support can make all the difference. In addition, we can build stronger relationships that stand the test of time by fostering communication, empathy, and mutual respect.

Another aspect is the misunderstanding of Women's Liberation, and Feminism is sometimes another factor for divorce.

So many people use the word feminism but do not truly understand its value and importance. Women's liberation: these words are commonly wrongfully used amongst women the majority of the time. If you can, please discover what women's liberation and feminism are.

Are these two concepts or movements the same?

Feminism or liberation, which one came first?

I have witnessed some women dissociating themselves from feminism, perceiving it as an extremist movement disconnected from the women's liberation movement. For example, do women's liberation ideals oppose marriage in our time? Does the idea that women are equal to men discourage men from tying the knot?

With the support of the women's liberation movement, many women have found the strength and determination to challenge situations where they feel deprived of equal opportunities in society. This is a fantastic concept, but some women extend it into their marriages and become the head of the household (an alpha female), as some men would subscribe. Of course, there's nothing wrong with being an alpha female; some people were born alpha females, and some developed it through life experiences. However, are you expressing it rightfully, or are you using it to your advantage against your partner?

In every relationship, there is a hierarchy. This is why God is the Almighty Being in heaven and on earth, a king is the leader of a monarchy, a president is the leader of a nation, a chief is the leader of a village, and every football team has a head coach. Similarly, there is always a head in every household. Who is the head of your home? Do you acknowledge and respect their authority?

You cannot reach your full potential in the wrong relationship. Always remember that it's not the right fit for you if you consistently get hurt in a relationship. Listen to your inner voice and walk away before you cause harm to yourself or others. Sometimes, that inner voice may be God guiding you.

If you or someone you know is suffering from any form of abusive relationship, please seek help before it's too late. Most people are aware of their inner voice and should recognise when enough is enough. (I will elaborate on the various types of abusive relationships later in this chapter.)

Why are relationships one of the most significant hurdles in life's journey?

ဆ 19 ଓ

The world is rapidly changing, and society is evolving at an astonishing pace, as is the state of our relationships. As a result, mental health has emerged as a fundamental factor in relationships nowadays, and the breakdown of relationships leads to feelings of anxiety, isolation, depression, and even suicide.

While technology, body image, fashion, and behaviour are all rapidly advancing, the truth remains that our primal brain is always on alert when we feel like we don't have a support system to rely on.

On reflection, our entire life revolves around relationships. From our relationship with the Creator and the universe to our connections with one another, these nourish us and make our everyday existence worthwhile. Despite our diverse religious and cultural backgrounds, we all require each other to thrive and flourish.

What are the most meaningful relationships to you and why?

From the moment we enter this world, our growth and development are deeply influenced by our family relationships. We are born into a family unit, and although we may not have had a say in who our parents are, we choose to love and accept them for who they are through our family relationships. Family dynamics shape our lives and can create patterns that follow us throughout our journey, like our DNA.

Childhood relationships play a crucial role in our mental and physical well-being. Children learn relationship patterns and behaviours from their families and embody these values as they grow older. Positive family relationships can build trust, promote healthy life skills, and lay the foundation for strong personal and interpersonal relationships. However, children raised in abusive households may struggle with reliving their traumatic childhood experiences in their adult lives.

As we age, we venture into the world, explore possibilities, make friendships, and form new connections. We learn about our boundaries and preferences and begin defining ourselves as individuals. This realisation helps us break free from familial expectations and beliefs, allowing our individuality to shine.

As we continue to navigate life, we understand that family is not just the one we are born into. Friends can be the family we choose for ourselves, as they provide support, companionship, and love that rival blood relatives. Some friendships become stronger than blood ties, and the relationships we form with them can be incredibly meaningful.

Research conducted by Harvard University has demonstrated the profound impact that friendships can have on our brains, affecting how we navigate the world around us. Notably, esteemed researcher Rebecca G. Adams of the University of North Carolina posited that "Friendship has a bigger impact on our psychological well-being than family relationships," a claim substantiated by scientific evidence. Regrettably, life can be unfair, and some individuals are born into families where they face neglect, abuse, and maltreatment or may have been orphaned and raised in foster care. However, if you are in such a situation, know that life offers endless possibilities.

It is important to note that your family need not be the bedrock of your relationships, and as we mature, we may discover that we require different things from our lives than what our families can offer. This is precisely why some individuals venture out and establish new families. Friendship can significantly shape our personalities and aspirations, allowing us to cultivate the lives we want to lead.

During the Covid-19 pandemic, a dear friend of mine, a lively extrovert, found it difficult to derive pleasure from her day-to-day activities. Her weekends were typically filled with volunteering, participating in group cooking classes, organising barbecues for the neighbourhood, and going on dates. Suddenly, her world turned upside down, and she had no one to turn to or anywhere to go during the lockdown. While we maintained regular contact through virtual platforms and checked in with each other at least twice a week, working from home meant that everyone was operating in different time zones. One morning, she called me in distress, her voice laden with tears as she described the profound sense of isolation she was experiencing.

"Are you alright, Fatima?" I inquired with worry and concern for my dear friend's well-being.

"They are tears of pure joy!" she exclaimed, her laughter ringing like music.

Naturally, I was taken aback and had to know more. Finally, she explained that her new neighbour, whom she had only met a few times, had surprised her with a homemade apple pie and a heartfelt note thanking her for her contributions to the community. It was a small yet meaningful gesture that touched her deeply and left her feeling appreciated and valued.

Her words touched my heart, prompting me to research acquaintances' impact on our lives. Despite my extensive knowledge of relationships, I had never considered the importance of casual acquaintances in our daily lives. However, my perspective shifted when I learned that these seemingly small and insignificant interactions could hold great value.

Studies have shown that we interact with an average of eleven to sixteen acquaintances on any given day, such as our bus driver, barista, mail carrier, or Uber driver. While brief, these spontaneous and light-hearted interactions can significantly benefit our well-being, including reducing the risk of burnout. Furthermore, acquaintances have the potential to become lasting friendships, a fact that we must not overlook.

And then there are our beloved colleagues, those enchanting, almost magical creatures who work hard, challenge us, and help us grow into our best selves. Colleagues provide us with invaluable opportunities to develop people skills, learn how to collaborate and be part of a team, and offer constructive feedback that helps us grow. Even in difficult situations or with challenging people, our colleagues teach us how to manage boundaries and become more resilient, reliable, and adaptable.

But this book isn't just about the many relationships surrounding us. Instead, it's about exploring the most important relationships that can shape our lives and make us feel truly whole: our romantic and family relationships. In her beautiful song, *Need to Be Next to You*, Sara Evans captures the essence of the emotions and feelings that romantic relationships inspire in us: "I need to know I can see your smile each morning. Look into your eyes each night. For the rest of my life, here with you, near with you. Oh, I need to be next to you. Right here with you is where I belong."

Love is a timeless, evergreen concept that ebbs and flows with the tides of time. For many, it's an elusive game that they seek to win. Some approach it with cruelty, tearing it down before it can flourish. Yet, some cherish it, working tirelessly to build lasting bonds with their families and loved ones. If you're struggling to cultivate meaningful relationships in your life, whether with a partner, family member, friend, or the divine, this book is the perfect guide for you.

From Chapter Two onwards, you'll be swept away on a journey with James, a masterful teacher of relationships whose wisdom and insight will leave you spellbound. James' faith, focus, favour, and determination are truly awe-inspiring. His unwavering discipline led him to achieve his vision of becoming a leader rather than a toil to his mindset. While not everyone is destined to be a leader, James' message is clear: Whatever you do, do it with excellence, for ultimately, you'll be alone with your thoughts and innermost self.

With a heart full of love and gratitude, I present *Human Beings and the Aspect of Relationships* to you. Writing this book has been a joyous experience and reading it can bring you the same level of joy and transformation that it has brought me. This book can revolutionise your thinking and way of life, so let it guide you towards more profound and meaningful relationships that last a lifetime.

> *The second phase of chapter one looks at some of the different aspects of abusive relationships. You can proceed to chapter two and return to this phase after reading chapter nine or continue reading this chapter to understand the following chapters better.*

Unhealthy relationships

In the past, I found myself in a misguided and troubled relationship, mistaking it for love. At first, my partner was a true gentleman, one of the kindest souls I had ever met. He doted on my children and was always there for me, even lending me his precious car — a clear sign of his affection. His gestures were sweet and affectionate, but it was short-lived.

My partner was plagued by insecurities that seeped into every aspect of our relationship. It started with petty jealousy over my Facebook friends' comments and calls on my phone, but soon it escalated. He criticised my clothing choices and discouraged me from spending time with my friends, whom he didn't approve of. Each day brought new accusations of infidelity or flirting, which became unbearable.

One night, while returning from a celebration with a dear friend, we found him waiting outside my home to check on me.

Unfortunately, this wasn't the first time, and his jealousy became increasingly suffocating. On another occasion, he followed us in his car after we went out for dinner. These events only cemented my decision to end the relationship, as I could see the insecurities taking root and potentially leading to lifelong consequences.

In retrospect, I learned that unhealthy relationships are like poison that slowly seeps into our lives, bringing devastation and pain. It takes immense courage to recognise the warning signs and walk away, but it's the only way to preserve our well-being and pave the way for healthier, more fulfilling relationships.

My dear friend and I were like two peas in a pod, inseparable and always there for each other through thick and thin. But our bond changed when she had a crush on a guy we both knew. I supported her with excitement, and we strategized together, planning the perfect moment for her to approach him. To our surprise, he asked her out to a friend's Christmas party, and they soon became inseparable. They spent their weekends exploring the town, holding hands, sharing secrets, and working out together.

But as much as I wanted my friend to be happy, I couldn't help but feel left out. She began cancelling plans with me to spend more time with him and even stood me up at a pub one night. I waited for over an hour, but she never showed up and didn't answer any of my calls. Finally, I started feeling uncomfortable with the situation, but my friend was head over heels and saw nothing wrong.

He continuously checked in on her, calling her multiple times when we hung out, and I couldn't help but feel like a third wheel. But in the end, we were young and naive, and didn't know any better. I thought this was what true love looked like — a sweet and caring guy who always wanted to be with her.

As young adults, my best friend and I were still learning the ways of the world, and we often made mistakes. Despite my doubts, I couldn't help but wonder if the relationship between her and the guy she was seeing was the definition of true love. One fateful night, I caught him holding hands with another girl at a club, and I knew I had to tell my friend the truth. Without thinking of the consequences, I revealed what I had seen to her.

To my relief, my friend trusted me and confronted him. He denied wrongdoing and even claimed that the other girl was his sister. My friend was willing to believe him, but I knew something wasn't right. He continued to lie, getting angrier and nastier with each question my friend asked. Eventually, he slammed the door in her face and demanded she never contact him again.

Despite my warnings, my friend refused to see the red flags in his behaviour. She spent days trying to make it up to him, sending him homemade treats and gifts, and even going to his house daily to apologise. He made her beg for his forgiveness, and when he finally spoke to her again, he played the victim and claimed to be hurt that she didn't trust him. My friend was overjoyed that he was talking to her again and didn't even remember the other girl he had been holding hands with.

THE ASPECT OF RELATIONSHIPS

They rekindled their relationship, but it wasn't long before my sweet friend caught him red-handed, kissing another girl at her birthday party! She was heartbroken, but I always stood by her side, ready to help her heal and grow stronger from the experience. This difficult time taught us valuable lessons about what to look for in a healthy relationship and how to recognise the warning signs that a relationship might be heading down an unhealthy path.

To help her cope, I surrounded my dear friend with love and support. I gave her a stack of books on healing from heartbreak and even shared one of my favourite books, Professor Joseph Murphy's inspiring and uplifting, *The Power of Your Subconscious Mind*. I wanted her to understand that just because she had been hurt before didn't mean she would be hurt again; she had the power to shape her destiny and create the loving and fulfilling relationship she deserved.

As we talked and reflected, I realised that my friend had been trapped in an unhealthy relationship pattern, driven by deep-seated beliefs about what it meant to be a good partner. Her parents, who were otherwise loving and wonderful, had modelled some unhealthy relationship dynamics. Her sweet, gentle mother had always been the peacekeeper in the family, soothing her father's temper when he came home stressed and sometimes took it out on her. Over time, my friend had learned to internalise that women must always work hard to keep a relationship going, even if that meant sacrificing their needs and happiness.

It's a common human experience to internalise beliefs and biases about relationships, passing them on unconsciously to those around us. But these biases can become heuristics that shape our thoughts and actions in unhealthy ways, leading even the most caring and trusting individuals down a path of pain and disappointment. So, I was grateful to have helped my friend break free from this pattern and find a way to healing and self-love.

But how can we become aware of the signs?

How can we discern if we are part of the unfortunate group caught in an unhealthy relationship or inadvertently contributing towards its demise? The answer is to cultivate an acute awareness of the defining traits of an unhealthy relationship.

Characteristics of an unhealthy relationship:

Unhealthy relationships can be identified by disrespect, lack of trust, absence of individuality, failure to understand each other, poor communication, self-centeredness, weak problem-solving abilities, and, most importantly, abuse. The following sections will examine these aspects in detail and explore how they can slowly seep into your relationships. But first, let's take a closer look at disrespect.

<u>Disrespect</u>

It is one of the most critical factors that can destroy a relationship. It is the foundation of all conflicts, leading to anger, resentment, and fear. But on the other hand, respect between partners creates a strong bond of safety, appreciation, and value.

Disrespect can manifest as rudeness, lack of empathy, disloyalty, and indifference. The truth is that disrespect leads to contempt, which ultimately leads to divorce or relationship breakdown.

However, it's important to remember that not all signs of disrespect are absolute. Your partner may exhibit a few or more of these behaviours without awareness.

Alternatively, past experiences or unresolved trauma may cause your partner to believe disrespect is routine in a relationship. You and your partner can work together to make the necessary changes for a healthy and fulfilling relationship by being aware of these behaviours and their impact.

1. The Power of Silence

How two individuals argue can reveal much about the level of respect in their relationship. Take, for instance, a work colleague from years ago who sought my advice. She confided in me that her husband would give her silent treatment whenever they disagreed. The silence was excruciating for her, leaving her feeling anxious and insecure. To her, their relationship should have been built on a foundation of mutual respect, where communication should always be present, even during tough times.

However, her husband's refusal to communicate with her made her feel she had done something wrong, leaving her wondering what she could have done differently. Over time, she altered her behaviour to avoid this punishment, which only worsened things. Eventually, the pain became too much for her to bear, and she made the difficult decision to divorce him.

While requesting space after a heated argument to collect your thoughts and emotions is natural, the silent treatment is entirely different. It does not stem from a place of mutual understanding or respect, like a mutually agreed-upon period of reflection. Instead, the silent treatment can manifest in a variety of ways, such as walking out in the middle of a conversation, refusing to answer calls or texts, remaining silent during attempts to communicate, or even locking oneself away in another room and refusing to respond to any attempts at communication.

As psychologist Dr Fran Walfish explains, "The silent treatment keeps you in suspense of what will happen and unsure of what you did wrong and how bad it is." It is a cruel form of abuse, also known as 'stonewalling,' and leads to a situation where the recipient of the silent treatment is denied the opportunity to express their needs, clarify misunderstandings, explain their situation, or even apologise. It creates a dead end that leads to no fair or just reconciliation.

2. **Ignoring your partner's voice**

In a healthy relationship, partners listen attentively to each other and take an active interest in what the other person says. However, when one partner consistently fails to listen, it can be a sign of disrespect and cause frustration, loneliness, and rejection. This can take the form of dismissal, where a partner simply ignores what the other person is saying, responds with one-word answers, or later claims to have forgotten what was discussed. This behaviour can make the other person feel insignificant and like their opinions and thoughts do not matter.

Another way a partner may ignore your voice is through unwarranted interruptions. While occasional interruptions are normal, interrupting constantly, interrupting with unimportant information, or interrupting to finish sentences can signal a lack of interest in the other person's perspective. This behaviour can make it difficult to express oneself, leading to misunderstandings and arguments.

Distraction is also a common sign of a partner not listening to you. For example, if a partner seems preoccupied with something else while you're trying to have a conversation, it can be a sign that they are not fully present and engaged with you. This can be particularly hurtful if you seek emotional support or validation, leading to feelings of rejection and disconnection.

While there may be underlying reasons for failing to listen, such as mental health issues or stress, both partners must recognise the importance of active listening in a healthy relationship. This behaviour can be improved with effort and commitment, leading to a more fulfilling and connected relationship.

3. Not upholding the sanctity of the union

Love takes many forms, and it's a beautiful thing. With modern advancements in human rights and scientific discoveries, we've come to appreciate that relationships are as diverse as the people who form them. Men can find love with other men and women with women, and some may even prefer the complexities of a topple or explore love with multiple partners. Every type of relationship can be fulfilling and meaningful to whoever chooses them. Still, when one or more partners fail to honour their commitments, the sanctity of the union is compromised.

It's essential to express your wants and needs before entering any relationship, and it's equally important to ensure that your partner(s) respect them. If one partner disregards the previously discussed matters of concern, it's a clear sign of disrespect. For instance, if a couple agrees that faithfulness is crucial, and one partner chooses to philander around town, it blatantly disregards the union's sanctity.

While I usually advise readers, clients, family and friends to address issues and try to work through them, there are cases when it's best to walk away from a relationship. When the trust and respect necessary for a healthy relationship are compromised, it's more than fair to consider ending the union.

4. Refusal to respect those important to you

While browsing *Reddit* for research purposes, I came across a touching personal story shared by a woman living in Malaysia. She expressed her struggle to understand how her relationship was unfolding. After dating her boyfriend for eight months, she met his family and even went on vacation with them. She assisted in decorating his sister's baby shower and spent money organising party favours. However, despite her efforts to integrate herself into his life, he did not try getting to know her family. She wondered if he was waiting for an indication of her interest.

Eventually, she invited him to drink with her sister at a specific time, 5:00 p.m. She called him from the bar at 5:15, and he claimed he was on his way. However, by 5:45, he said he was heading back because of traffic. She was disappointed but chose to spend the evening with her sister instead.

She wrote, "I felt embarrassed. My sister suggested he was lying, but I knew he wasn't. Why would he? Maybe there was traffic."

Several weeks later, she invited him to lunch with her parents, who prepared a delicious roast chicken, and her father had ice-cold beer ready. However, he didn't show up because his phone was unreachable. He eventually arrived an hour after everyone had eaten, blaming it on his dead phone battery.

As I read through her story, it became apparent that he took advantage of what she brought to the relationship. However, he lacked respect for her, her loved ones, and her cherished relationships.

In a loving partnership, it's important to adore your significant other and cherish their friends and family. Therefore, being respectful and courteous is essential. Unfortunately, some partners fall short in this area, and their disrespectful behaviour towards you and your loved ones can be evident in various ways. For example:

- They consistently arrive late to family events, showing little regard for their effort to organise everything.

- They act as if socialising with important people in your life is daunting, making you feel embarrassed and disrespected.

- They exhibit a condescending attitude and passive-aggressive behaviour at gatherings, causing discomfort and tension among the group.

- They make belittling comparisons between your family and theirs, creating an unnecessary rift and disrespecting your roots.

At the end of the day, romantic relationships should bring joy and value to all aspects of your life, including relationships with friends and family.

5. Trust Issues

Trust is the foundation of any relationship. Things can quickly go awry without it, leading to conflict and sometimes even violence. It can start with small things like a suggestion to open a joint bank account, which might later lead to one partner obsessively tracking the other's spending habits or controlling them financially.

I once spoke to a man whose girlfriend installed a GPS tracking app on his phone because she claimed she was worried about his safety. Then, one night, he changed his mind and decided to go out with his sister instead of staying home, as he had initially planned.

His girlfriend noticed the change in his location and showed up at his sister's house, causing a scene and accusing him of lying and betrayal. Unfortunately, the relationship didn't last long after that incident.

As he recounted his experience, I could feel the pain and betrayal he must have felt. Lack of trust can cause immense emotional turmoil and lead to conflicts that are difficult to resolve. Cell phone snooping is often a partial mediator of relationship conflicts and the intention to break up.

In any relationship, there's always a risk of getting hurt or disappointed. However, secure and stable people seek relationships where they can find respite and comfort, knowing they are with a partner they can trust and trust in return.

Indulge me as I spin a more eloquent tale with the most saccharine of words!

Lack of trust can rear its ugly head in numerous ways: Rifling through cherished personal treasures, like treasured cell phones and laptops, in search of supposed clues.

Eavesdropping on the most intimate of conversations, popping up unannounced at routine haunts (such as at your workplace) under the guise of "dropping by"; making intrusive calls to family and friends, inquiring about your whereabouts, and a host of other unsettling habits.

Sadly, an absence of trust often harkens back to bygone traumas, leaving partners powerless to bestow the necessary sense of safety. Sometimes, it takes the touch of a professional to help overcome such challenges. A partner who loathes trusting will more often than not grapple with gloom and insomnia and even engage in clandestine, passive-aggressive behaviour. When confronted, they'll likely rationalise their conduct, bemoaning how their past misadventures engendered this defensive stance.

Staying within such a relationship without actively addressing the underlying causes of unease can only compound feelings of anxiety and desolation. When navigating such situations, it's imperative to bear in mind your requirements, lest you become mired in efforts to placate a partner's perpetual distrust.

6. Lack of individuality

Let me grace this passage with a more mellifluous language fit for a poetic soul!

Individuality is a precious jewel in any romantic liaison's crown. Alas, all too frequently, lovers regard each other as mere chattel whose sole purpose is to serve as a mirror of their being. It's important to remember that you are your unique entity, and your partner is also. For instance, marriages are arranged in certain cultures, with prescribed gender roles firmly in place. In some parts of Asia and Africa, women lose their lives for dishonouring their families by not adhering to the norms of their husband's clans. While such occurrences may be more prevalent in certain areas, the principle remains the same: when one partner is expected to mild themselves to fit the other, and their beliefs and desires are deemed "selfish," the relationship warrants examination.

The essence of any romantic entanglement is cooperation towards common goals without one partner forfeiting their essence. In Western societies, this can manifest in a subtle moulding of oneself to fit the other's image in societies. If you find yourself stuck in a prescribed role within a relationship without knowing how you ended up there, it's time to reevaluate. Do you revolve your life around your partner's whims? Is your career sacrificed to support your partner's ambitions? Are you deprived of "me time"? Are even minor tasks, like opening a bank account, beyond your reach without your partner's assistance? Do you feel intimidated to voice your desires?

Lack of individuality often creeps in through covert, controlling tactics. Examples include belittling your passions and interests, dictating what you wear, censoring your speech in public, expecting you to shelve your plans for your partner's benefit, hindering your social circle to an approved list, or even guilt-tripping you for taking time for yourself. Such behaviour robs you of your independence and stifles the blossoming of a genuinely loving relationship.

A relationship lacking individuality can suffocate and harm one's sense of self. When your partner disregards your interests and passions, you may begin to feel as though you are losing touch with who you truly are. This can cause you to feel adrift and disconnected from others who share your background and values. You may even doubt your worth and submit to your partner's desires, surrendering control over your life.

It is essential to understand that a relationship built on such a foundation of control and conformity is unhealthy. Cultivating your individuality and pursuing your passions is important, as this will benefit you and enhance your relationship with your partner. By embracing and supporting each other's unique interests and strengths, you can build a solid and respectful bond that allows both of you to grow and thrive as individuals.

7. Lack of understanding

Sometimes, an unhealthy relationship can stem not from unhealthy beliefs or behaviours but from a lack of compatibility. Compatibility refers to the ability of two or more people to work seamlessly together without needing to change any part of themselves. Ola, for example, was born to a Nigerian mother and a French father in West Africa, and due to his parents' frequent country hopping, he developed an insatiable taste for adventure. As a result, he always craved excitement and spontaneity in life and felt constricted when he lacked them.

After turning 18, Ola moved to the West to attend university and later found a job in New York, where he met Sophia, his future wife. Sophia had always dreamt of marriage, and Ola, a sweet, charming man, felt ready for it too. So, after six months of dating, he proposed, and they married shortly after. However, they failed to realise that they didn't know each other long enough to make such a monumental decision, and their first major disagreement was rooted in an assumption they had never known about themselves.

Ola had always dreamed of finding a marriage as wonderful as his parents' fairy tale romance. He believed that even if things didn't work out, he could get a divorce and move on. Therefore, he didn't feel the need to put extra pressure on himself to "make a marriage work." On the other hand, Sophia had a difficult childhood, growing up between two homes due to her parent's divorce when she was only eight. The trauma from that experience stayed with her for years, making her hesitant to trust anyone enough to enter a serious relationship. She believed that any relationship worth her time should last a lifetime and was determined to do everything she could to ensure that she and Ola never got a divorce.

Things were more complicated than just their differing views on divorce, though. While Ola knew exactly what he wanted out of life, Sophia was still figuring things out and struggling to understand herself. As a result, Sophia grew increasingly insecure as time passed, while Ola became increasingly unhappy and resentful. For example, Ola enjoyed spending his weekends outdoors with his friends, fishing, camping, and sometimes partying. He would invite Sophia along, but she wasn't much of an outdoors person and would often accuse him of not wanting to spend time with her. This couldn't have been further from the truth!

Ola didn't want to purchase an apartment in New York because he felt it would tie him down. The down payment alone was well over a hundred thousand dollars, and the prospect of owning property made him uneasy. Sophia, however, couldn't understand why he wouldn't want to start a life with her, especially since they were already married.

When she brought it up, Ola was surprised, saying, "I thought we had already started our lives when we got married."

A year later, Ola discussed having children, and Sophia was overjoyed to be on board. But then, Ola was offered a new job in Singapore, and he excitedly told Sophia, assuming she would be just as thrilled about the opportunity to travel. Instead, that night, they had a huge fight. Sophia called him selfish for not discussing it with her first. Ola tried to calm her down by explaining the situation, but tensions were high.

Sophia could work from any location on the planet, meaning they could still visit their loved ones whenever they wanted. Despite this, Ola didn't inform Sophia about the job opportunity he had received. He didn't want her to feel sorry for him if he was rejected.

However, the position offered double his current salary, and the tax bracket in Singapore was only 16%, a prospect that intrigued him. Ola adored travelling to different parts of the world, and he believed that Sophia shared his passion. But, of course, he would never go against Sophia's wishes.

Therefore, Ola couldn't comprehend why Sophia was so upset. He hadn't even accepted the job offer yet. He just wanted to discuss it with her before deciding.

Sophia was still fuming with anger. You know that moment when you're so scared of something that you can't think rationally and are not open to listening to reason? Sophia had withdrawn into herself and left to spend time with her parents. She requested space, and Ola was never one to be frightened of space. So, he gave her what she required.

A week later, they decided to meet over coffee and try to work things out. During their discussion, Sophia observed a pattern. How could they have children in Singapore? What if they had to move again in a few years? Would their children be displaced and never have a place to call home? Would they miss out on spending time with their families? Sophia was terrified, thinking that moving to Singapore would ruin the future she had planned for their imaginary kids. Eventually, the couple agreed to seek help from a couple's therapist, and their session revealed why they were struggling to communicate with each other.

Ola grew up in an ever-changing environment, which gave him a sense of security. Sophia also experienced a turbulent childhood, but her difficulties stemmed from her parent's divorce. As a result, any change from her past, even positive ones like when her mother relocated to New Jersey and Sophia had to change schools, was associated with the divorce and viewed as a disruption.

After undergoing months of therapy, Sophia and Ola could finally comprehend each other. Ola understood that change was difficult for Sophia, while Sophia learned that Ola thrived under it. As a result, they made compromises and met in the middle, understanding each other better and becoming more compatible.

This story highlights the importance of shared understanding between partners. If your partner displays any of the following signs or complaints, you may not be compatible because you need to understand each other better. Nevertheless, as illustrated above, there is always room for improvement.

Signs that indicate a lack of understanding include your partner not comprehending how you spend your time and complaining about you wanting to spend too much time alone. You and your partner may also argue over finances, child-rearing, or political matters, and it is important to find common ground. Additionally, you may view your partner as messy, while they do not see it that way, or you may disagree on basic cleanliness habits, such as leaving dishes in the sink overnight.

Even small misunderstandings can accumulate and cause significant rifts in a relationship. Therefore, it is advisable to try and understand your partner as much as possible before committing to them for life and to work actively and deliberately towards resolving any misunderstandings, much like Sophia and Ola did.

8. *No compromise*

In the movie, *Shall We Dance?* Beverly Clark poses a profound question, "Why do people get married?" She responds with a sentiment so poignant and beautiful that it lingers long after the movie ends. She says, "We need a witness to our lives. There are a billion people on the planet... I mean, what does anyone's life really mean? But in a marriage, you promise to care about everything. The good things, the bad things, the terrible things, the mundane things…all of it, all the time, every day. You're saying, 'Your life will not go unnoticed because I will notice it. Your life will not go unwitnessed because I will be your witness.'"

This is the essence of human connection that has allowed our species and every animal species to flourish. Connection helps us protect one another, which gives rise to a future where we can all be safe and thrive.

But promising to care about everything means doing the small, joyous things that make up a relationship. It means showing up for the happy moments and toasting your partner's promotion. It means snuggling with them when cold and making them a warm cup of coffee when burning the midnight oil.

The hard part, however, is compromising when necessary. For a relationship to work, both partners must be willing to make compromises. Compromises can be challenging but essential to creating a healthy and thriving relationship.

In a relationship without compromise, one partner constantly takes while the other gives. It's a heartbreaking situation where one person is left on the sidelines, watching their partner's life unfold without their own being witnessed with equal love. It's a one-sided relationship, like a parasitic leech attached to a flourishing tree, draining it of all its vitality.

Often, the giver in such relationships has a heart so pure and selfless that they don't realise how unfair the situation is. When a kind, empathetic soul falls for a selfish, uncompromising person, it's a true test of how much compromise a generous person can make and how stubborn a selfish person can be. It's a clash of two extremes, and as time passes, one person begins to desire more while the other starts to resent giving so much.

A relationship that lacks balanced compromises is incredibly unhealthy. It's toxic for chronic compromisers, who can end up feeling drained and taken advantage of. However, I've seen beautiful relationships where one partner notices their significant other always compromising and consciously tries not to take advantage. It's a heart-warming situation where someone else is looking out for their needs.

But in a relationship where no one is looking out for your needs, you must learn to look out for yourself. Compromise is necessary, but always compromising is wrong. You must meet each other halfway and reach an agreement that works for both of you. It's essential to be aware of both your and your partner's needs. If your partner is making more compromises, you must support them in a healthier way by making compromises of your own. If your partner always expects you to compromise, you must prioritise your needs. A caring, loving partner would be concerned about your needs; if they're not, that's a worrying sign.

9. *Delicate Communication*

The art of communication is a beautiful and vital aspect of any successful relationship. Delicate communication encompasses a broad spectrum of situations, from actively listening and comprehending to engaging in thoughtful conversation without ulterior motives. Unfortunately, some individuals engage in psychological warfare, such as lying and gaslighting, which ultimately leads to damaging consequences for their partner.

Several tell-tale signs of struggling with delicate communication include pretending to listen but not absorbing the information, interrupting one's partner, and failing to follow through with instructions or requests. These behaviours create a sense of unease and lack of trust in the relationship.

Gaslighting is a severe form of poor communication often employed by narcissists. The ramifications of gaslighting can be significant and cause immense anxiety and depression for the partner on the receiving end. For example, a simple miscommunication regarding the meeting time could be used as a tactic to manipulate and control one's partner.

I once worked with a client who struggled with severe depression and anxiety after being in a relationship with a narcissist for a year. In retrospect, it was evident that delicate communication was absent from the beginning. The client would arrive on time for dates, but her partner would always be late and blame her for not listening to the correct time.

Despite her efforts to confirm plans through texts and writing them down, her partner continued to blame her for his tardiness.

Strong and delicate communication is fundamental to building a solid foundation of trust, security, and understanding in a relationship.

10. *Self-centred love*

It can be a devastating experience for those on the receiving end. Some enter relationships to build a life together that benefits both individuals, and some enter relationships solely to fill a void within themselves. Selfish love is something that no one should have to endure. It is a love concerned exclusively with serving its own needs and desires, holding back, and hindering the growth and fulfilment of the other person involved. This kind of love can manifest in various ways in a relationship, such as a partner who only cares about what they want and has no regard for their partner's desires and needs. Such people often believe their partner should feel grateful and fortunate to be in a relationship with them. For instance, a woman who expects her partner to earn a certain amount of money each year or threatens to leave him if he doesn't, or a man who demands that his wife quit her job to manage his household and ensure that there is always a home-cooked meal waiting for him when he comes home.

Selfish love can also be demonstrated by a partner who disregards the other person's desires in intimate situations.

Individuals with self-centred needs will only put in the effort until they receive what they want in the bedroom. If you express your desires, you might be shunned, ignored, mocked, or given excuses. These are just a few examples of how selfish love can manifest. However, it is important to note that not all selfish love is inherently bad. Sometimes, partners may struggle to effectively communicate what they want from a relationship, which can lead to a self-fulfilling prophecy in which one partner is left feeling like they are in love with someone who is selfish. In these situations, it is essential to clearly communicate what is needed in the relationship to avoid misunderstandings and resentment.

Characteristics of Healthy Relationships:

A healthy relationship is like a soothing balm for the soul that nurtures and rejuvenates an individual in countless ways. It brings joy and fulfilment and profoundly benefits one's overall well-being. Research reveals that a happy and healthy relationship can positively impact physical health. Being in a healthy relationship means lower rates of depression and anxiety, increased self-esteem, and even better heart health due to reduced stress levels.

A healthy relationship is a beautiful journey of two people growing together, evolving, and becoming the best versions of themselves. It's better to be single than be in a toxic relationship that can harm one's health and happiness. Unfortunately, people often stay in unhealthy relationships because they do not know what a healthy relationship looks like or are afraid of being alone. This book teaches you how to have the love you deserve and create a healthy relationship.

Healthy relationships are founded on a strong foundation of values such as respect, trust, individuality, understanding, compromise, open and honest communication, empathy, and selfless love. These pillars of healthy relationships are the exact opposite of what defines unhealthy relationships.

1. *Respect*

Love and respect go hand in hand, and a relationship filled with respect is truly beautiful. When two individuals respect each other, it creates a foundation of trust, appreciation, and understanding.

Respect means valuing your partner as an individual with their unique thoughts, feelings, and desires. It means recognising and accepting their flaws and imperfections and not trying to change them to fit your expectations.

In a respectful relationship, disagreements are handled with care and consideration. Both parties strive to understand each other's perspectives and work together to find a solution that works for both. Each person's opinions are valued, and neither partner tries to dominate or control the other.

Appreciation is also an essential aspect of respect. Small acts of kindness and thoughtfulness are never taken for granted, and both partners express gratitude for each other's efforts. This creates a sense of mutual admiration and deepens the bond between partners.

A relationship based on respect extends beyond the private sphere of the couple. Partners who respect each other also show that respect in public, whether with friends or family. They present a united front and support each other in all aspects of life.

Overall, respect is not just given but earned through a continuous effort to understand and value your partner as an individual. Both partners feel seen, heard, and appreciated in a respectful relationship, creating a strong foundation for a healthy and loving partnership.

2. *Trust*

Would you like to constantly live in fear of the unknown? Most people would say no. Instead, a happy and fulfilling life is one where you can confidently look towards the future. This optimistic view of the future is rooted in the trust you have in your partner. A relationship built on trust eliminates insecurities and fears, as you know your partner will not intentionally betray your trust.

Here are some sweet and loving ways to show that you trust your partner:

- Show your partner that you have faith in them by giving them the benefit of the doubt. You don't require constant reassurance or proof of their loyalty; you respect their privacy. In return, your partner feels secure and comfortable sharing their vulnerabilities and joys with you.

- Share personal matters with your partner, knowing that their advice and guidance will benefit you.

- Keep your partner's needs and wants in mind and be supportive of their individual goals and dreams.

- Allow your partner to maintain relationships with people you don't know and trust that they will make wise choices.

- Refrain from snooping or prying into private matters your partner is not ready to share with you. Trust that they will reveal the information when they are comfortable doing so.

- Be honest with your partner, even when you make mistakes. You know that your partner will appreciate your honesty and sincerity.

Being in a loving relationship built on mutual trust is the greatest gift in life. It allows you to cherish each other and embrace the future with optimism and confidence.

3. *Individuality*

A thriving relationship is one that allows for individuality to flourish. The most enchanting relationships are those where partners acknowledge and appreciate each other's unique strengths and weaknesses. I was recently at a small, intimate wedding where the maid of honour delivered a speech that truly encapsulated the importance of individuality.

She said, "Bami is a doer. He rises at the crack of dawn every morning. Jeneba, on the other hand, is a dreamer. She snoozes until noon and then rushes to Bami's study with her ambitious life plans. Months pass, and Jeneba still dreams while Bami keeps doing. Jeneba's only contribution to this wedding was dreaming that it would happen. But as Bami always says, we're lucky she remembered the date and showed up in a white dress!"

The guests chuckled because this story perfectly captured the essence of Jeneba and Bami's relationship. I've known them for years and seen how Jeneba's whimsy complements Bami's roundedness. She forgets everything while he carries his to-do list everywhere. They've never tried to change each other. In fact, they appreciate each other's differences. Without Jeneba, Bami would probably be too serious all the time, and without Bami, Jeneba would be lost on the subway. They need each other, and they help each other! Every time Bami runs out of marketing ideas for his digital marketing firm, a brief conversation with Jeneba gets him back on track. She's creative, and he's productive.

That's what individuality can bring to a relationship. To foster individuality in your relationship, try the following:

Find the time to pursue your passions and cultivate a strong identity. Encourage your partner to do the same!

Make time for yourself to discover who you truly are.

True happiness comes from within, so cultivate your ability to function independently and be content with that. It will make your relationship stronger!

Maintain your boundaries and know when to say no. This will help your partner better understand who you are and ultimately provide better support for you in the long run.

4. *Understanding*

Imagine this: You're at a lively party surrounded by chatty people but can't find your place in the crowd. Maybe you're an introvert feeling overwhelmed by all the noise or an extrovert growing tired of shallow small talk. You start stumbling over your words, second-guessing everything you say, and feeling anxious about being misunderstood. All you can do is hope for the night to end so you can finally relax and be yourself again.

That feeling of relief you experience when you finally get to be alone and free is what a healthy relationship should feel like. It's a safe space where you can always be yourself without fear of judgment or misunderstanding. But on the other hand, an unhealthy relationship can leave you feeling suffocated and anxious, without room for understanding.

To build understanding in your relationship, it's important to take the time to truly get to know your partner for who they are. Don't assume their behaviour is a reflection of yours, but instead, take an interest in their passions and preferences. Make little notes of what they like and don't like, and always respect their boundaries. Gautama Buddha once said, "True love is born from understanding." By trying to understand your partner, you can cultivate a deep and meaningful connection that will help you become the best version of yourselves.

5. *Compromise*

A one-sided relationship is a disservice to both parties. Love is a beautiful thing that inspires us to make our loved ones happy. It motivates us to prepare breakfast, leave sweet notes in the mirror, and plan surprise birthday parties. But shouldn't we also expect the same effort in return? Of course, we do.

However, the modern definition of compromise has negative connotations. It's often associated with sacrifice and loss. Compromising in a relationship doesn't mean we must relinquish our personal choices. It's quite the opposite. Compromise means we value our partner's happiness because their joy enriches our relationship.

Compromise is not giving up your personal choices but rather bringing happiness into your relationship. Here are some ways to incorporate compromise into a healthy relationship:

Make decisions together. If you're living together, ask your partner about their living space preferences. Ensure that both of you have little nooks and corners in the house that feel like home. If your partner wants a television in the bedroom, let them have it, but they can't put a pool table in the study you work in. It's about given and take.

Surrender small things that don't matter if the reward is more significant. For instance, if you're not a fan of almond milk, but your partner is lactose intolerant, you can compromise by swapping dairy milk for almond milk.

Share responsibilities. You can do the laundry on Fridays if your partner promises to cook on Sundays. Compromise is about meeting halfway and inclusively finding balance.

6. *Effective Communication*

Nurturing a healthy relationship requires effective communication skills.

Communication brings harmony, deep understanding, and the feeling of being heard. When done correctly, it can be a source of intimacy and connection between partners.

To start, it is essential to cultivate good communication habits, especially when disagreements or misunderstandings arise. Rather than arguing, it's better to have a list of guidelines to refer to in such instances. These guidelines can be used to resolve issues amicably and without conflict.

Here are a few examples of good communication habits:

1. Active listening is essential in any healthy relationship. Allow your partner to express themselves freely and without interruptions. Afterwards, take a few seconds to process what they said before responding.

2. Ambiguity creates confusion, so it's best to be clear and concise with your instructions. If necessary, write down what you want to say to avoid misinterpretation.

3. Authenticity is critical. Communicating your feelings and needs honestly and clearly without fear of judgment is essential. Authenticity fosters trust and respect between partners.

4. Choose words that convey respect, especially when angry or upset. Raising your voice, using foul language, or hurting your partner with exaggerated speech or words is unacceptable. Instead, communicate with kindness, empathy, and understanding.

   Remember, a healthy relationship thrives on open, honest communication that brings partners closer together. Avoid tactics like passive-aggressiveness, snappiness, gaslighting, and lying, which can destroy even the strongest bonds.

7. *Nurturing Affection for Others at the Core*

   Nurture a loving relationship that puts the needs of both parties at the forefront. Selfishness has no place in a healthy partnership. When you prioritise your partner, actively supporting each other's dreams and aspirations is important.

For instance, if you want to attend classes at a nearby college, your partner might work overtime to support you, or if your partner receives a fantastic job offer in another city, you may offer to move together.

Delight in your partner's happiness and take pleasure in their passions. Learn what makes them happy and appreciate their unique interests. Be attentive to your partner's desires, including their preferences in the bedroom.

Helen Keller once said, "The best and most beautiful things in the world cannot be seen or even touched — they must be felt with the heart." So, likewise, a healthy and loving relationship is felt with the heart and brings peace rather than anxiety.

You may be wondering, "Can unhealthy relationships be fixed? And are healthy relationships completely devoid of issues?" While some toxic relationships are beyond repair and require an immediate end, others can be mended through education and practical tools. Cherish your healthy relationship and continue to cultivate it with love and care. This book will provide the tools to leave toxicity behind, heal from past traumas, and enrich your relationship with even more warmth and light.

Chapter Two

The Divine Factor – Keeping the Focus on the Main Thing.

This chapter focuses on our relationship with God, having an individual relationship with God first and having a relationship with God as a couple; it also discusses the benefits of having God as the centre of our relationships. This chapter leads us to the introduction of the main character, James Tapia Kanu, and we follow his journey through spirituality and meeting his soulmate, Olivia.

The Divine Factor – Keeping the Focus on the Main Thing

> *"We are all blessed with the power to choose our path in life. We can choose to walk in the light or shadows, embrace happiness or succumb to sadness, and choose life or death. Our actions have consequences, and we hold ourselves accountable for them."*

The room was bathed in a warm glow from the sun's rays, seeping through the only window. The light seemed to caress his face, casting a gentle radiance that was both peaceful and divine. Although his posture on the bed was far from perfect due to continuous drinking the previous night, his face had a serene expression.

As he drifted into a deep slumber, he found himself lost in a dense forest, trying to navigate its depths. Fearing the creatures that lurked in the shadows, he suddenly saw a Tabor divine light that guided him towards his destination. Following the light, he arrived at his house, sprinting up the stairs to his balcony in terror.

There, he saw an angelic figure suspended in mid-air on the left side of the balcony, surrounded by a heavenly glow. Brian was standing on the right side, looking on in awe. James called out to him, asking if he could see the angel, and Brian replied, "She's pointing towards you; it appears like she is trying to tell you something."

Overcome by fear, James ran downstairs to get his brother, David, but he was too engrossed in his phone call to pay attention to James. Returning to the balcony, he saw the angelic figure still waiting to deliver her message. Too scared to listen, James ran out of the house and watched the figure disappear into a brilliant star in the sky.

Panicked and in disbelief, James sought refuge in Brian's home. He recounted his experience to Brian, who listened intently, explaining that he had a visit from one of the most extraordinary angels of all time. He warned James that she would return to deliver her message, and James needed to be ready to listen.

A distant bell rang as they spoke, breaking the moment's silence. James awoke with a start, realising that it had all been a dream. Nevertheless, the experience had felt so real that he trembled in fear at the memory.

These delightful dreams continued to return, growing more vivid with each occurrence. James rested peacefully on his bed, contemplating the significance of his visions. The soft melody of the alarm clock chimed five times, but the allure of slumber held him captive. Eventually, he roused himself around 10 in the morning, greeted by the gentle warmth of the sun's rays beaming upon his face. Groggy and disoriented, James struggled to open his eyes and battled a nagging headache.

He stepped into the shower, and the soothing water brought him back to his senses. Yet, his thoughts lingered on the elusive meaning of his dream. He glanced around his cluttered room, deciding to brew a cup of tea and tidy up. While cleaning, he noticed several missed calls from his friend, Brian.

"Good day, James!" Brian greeted him.

"Hello there," James responded with a solemn tone.

"Why did you miss the group study this morning?" Brian asked.

"I... I couldn't wake up," James confessed, wincing at his headache.

"Did you indulge in drinking again?" Brian queried.

"Yes," James replied, his voice soft and remorseful.

"Oh dear," Brian exhaled deeply. "Alright, let's meet up at Rose Café."

After hanging up the phone, James collapsed onto his bed again, abandoning the cleaning for the day. His eyes felt heavy,

THE DIVINE FACTOR – KEEPING THE FOCUS ON THE MAIN THING

and the thought of sleeping for the rest of the day was tempting, as it often was. Living in a hostel and being a student in London, James craved closer family or friend connections. His introverted nature limited him to staying focused on his tasks and keeping to himself. In his final year of university, he felt uncertain about his future and unsure of what to do once he graduated.

James observed the beautiful and tranquil surroundings as he strolled towards the café to meet his friend. The sun shone brightly, but the warmth was not oppressive, and people were enjoying themselves outside the café. Groups of four to six people sat at each table, their joyful laughter and content expressions adding to the already pleasant ambience. Across the way, seven builders were working diligently in the parking lot, undisturbed by the bustling crowd. The atmosphere was calm and serene; even the workers' faces were aglow with joy.

During their lunch, Brian briefed James on the group's discussion that morning. As he described the points, Brian noticed James' gaunt appearance.

"Are you alright?" Brian asked, concerned.

"I'm fine," James replied, though he sounded fatigued.

"It seems like something's bothering you," Brian said with a sympathetic expression.

"I'm just feeling a slight headache," James said with a weak smile.

"My dear friend, didn't I kindly advise you to be mindful of your drinking habits? We had this conversation just last week, and I can see that you may have repeated some questionable behaviour," Brian said in a soft and caring voice, trying to understand James' struggles.

As James tried to explain himself, Brian noticed that his friend's body and mind were not functioning as well as they could. He knew that James was facing challenges in his academic and personal life, and he wanted to offer his support and encouragement.

"Please don't be too hard on yourself, my dear friend. I believe in you, and I know that you have the potential to achieve great things," Brian said, putting a comforting hand on James' shoulder.

He listened attentively as James shared his frustrations and doubts about his life and future. Brian knew James was a complex and sensitive person who needed compassion and understanding.

"I understand that you may be feeling lost and uncertain about your purpose in life, but please don't give up hope. You have so much to offer the world, and I know that you will find your way," Brian said, speaking from his heart.

He gently urged James to attend a seminar on campus by a wise and experienced scholar, hoping that it might help him gain new insights and perspectives on his life. James initially hesitated, but Brian's kind and persuasive words eventually convinced him to try it.

As they listened to the scholar's sweet and calming voice, Brian could see that James was starting to relax and open up to new possibilities. He knew his friend still had a long way to go, but he was confident that James would find his path and achieve his dreams.

You are the most important person in your life, and your well-being should be your top priority. Take the time to understand your mind and the world around you and learn the true meaning of love and how to cultivate it. Life is about more than just chasing money; it's about making small but significant changes in your behaviour, mindset, and attitude, and learning to forgive the limitations of others. So, I ask you: what is the key to inner peace, and how can you attain it?

Firstly, it is essential to acknowledge that there's a greater being who created heaven and earth. Accept yourself for who you are and forgive your limitations, focus on yourself and surround yourself with positive energy. Live your life according to your means, learn to meditate and filter negative thoughts away from your mind. And finally, talk to God frequently; through prayers or conversations with yourself.

As the scholar spoke, James was transfixed by his words. His message resonated with James so deeply that he couldn't take his eyes off the speaker. He was in awe of the scholar's ability to easily connect with the audience and convey such powerful ideas.

After the lecture, James eagerly approached the scholar, introducing himself and expressing his admiration for the presentation. The scholar's smile and aura were contagious, radiating peace and tranquillity. James couldn't help but notice how content and fulfilled the scholar appeared.

"Is it because of mental peace?" James asked inquisitively.

The scholar nodded and replied, "Yes, it's all thanks to mental peace and well-being."

James was eager to know how he could attain such inner peace. The scholar answered simply yet profoundly: "Listen to your thoughts and filter them."

James left the encounter feeling inspired and motivated to change his life. The scholar's words awakened something deep within him, and he longed to achieve the same contentment and happiness.

Despite the mounting pressure of exams, James found solace in the scholar's teachings. He began to practice mindfulness and reflection, filtering his thoughts to prioritise his well-being. Slowly but surely, he felt a shift within himself, and his approach to life became more positive and centred.

The scholar's message profoundly impacted James, and he continued to draw inspiration from his teachings long after the lecture.

On the day before the exams, James was taking a stroll through the vibrant streets of London, trying to escape the pressure and intensity of exam season. He found himself in Trafalgar Square, surrounded by the buzz of tourists and locals. Suddenly, he heard a familiar voice call out his name. Turning around, he saw his friend, Brian, walking towards him with a pile of books in his hands. "Hey, James! What are you doing out here? Don't tell me you haven't been studying for the exams!" Brian said with a teasing smile.

James looked at his friend with a troubled expression on his face. "I just needed a break," he replied softly.

Brian saw the distress in James' eyes and asked, "Is everything alright?"

James hesitated momentarily before admitting, "No, not really."

Without hesitation, Brian suggested, "Hey, I know of a great lecture by that scholar you liked the other day. Maybe it will help clear your mind?" James felt a sudden spark of hope and nodded his head eagerly.

Together, they hopped into a black cab and headed towards East London. When they arrived, the same scholar lectured on improving relationships and the factors that influence them. Again, James was captivated by the scholar's words and the warmth and kindness that radiated from his being. As the lecture continued, the scholar began to speak about the God Factor and the role of belief in building strong relationships. Again, James listened intently, feeling a sense of peace wash over him as he absorbed the scholar's wisdom.

"One of the things that play an important role in strengthening a relationship is the God Factor. And I'm sad to say that; unfortunately, we ignore that leading factor in our lives. The God factor is nothing special that you didn't know. Nor is it a kind of rocket science that needs hours to understand. I refer to the God Factor as the Belief System.

"Your belief system is the building block in constructing a skyscraper of relationship. Whenever I talk about the role of God in relationships, I see emerging lines on your foreheads. Most people don't even consider it as a leading factor in any kind of relationship, and the rest of them call me holiest or Sufi for discussing it.

"But the truth is that your relationship with God affects your social life to a great extent. Therefore, the type of relationship you have with God, either healthy or unhealthy, is the same relationship you are dealing with in your daily life journey.

"I know my words will seem quite ridiculous to most of you. Nobody had trained us to think of our relationship with God. But if you ponder deeply on your relationships with your family and friends, you'll see that you somehow have that same kind of relationship with God or the universe."

James then realised that the God Factor was not just a religious concept but a fundamental aspect of our lives that influenced our relationships with others. The audience sat in rapt attention, completely absorbed by the scholar's words. James felt a newfound sense of hope and clarity as the lecture ended. He knew the road ahead would be challenging, but he was ready to face it with a renewed sense of purpose and a deeper understanding of the world around him.

My dear readers, I implore you to lend me your ears as I recount the wisdom shared by the learned scholar. Though his words may seem unconventional, they hold great truth and are worth pondering deeply.

As you reflect on the relationships you share with your loved ones, you will see that these relationships resemble the ones you share with God or the universe. And though we may not have been taught to think about our relationship with God, we are all part of the divine, and the divine is part of us. Therefore, it is through knowing and being aware of who we truly are that we know and understand God.

The scholar's teachings resonated deeply with James, and he could not help but express his admiration for him. And what a gracious and humble response he received in return!

James went near him, and after shaking his hand, he said, "You are a high-class spiritual scholar!"

"I'm not," replied the scholar. "Everyone is at the peak of spirituality and self-knowledge when you discover your purpose in life and who you truly are," he added softly.

"I will love to spend more time with you or people like you," James couldn't control himself from saying.

The scholar turned his face towards James fully. Brian and James could see the shine in his eyes that emerged instantaneously after hearing James' words. "You can," he replied. "Furthermore, it will be a great pleasure for me. I can guide you about it in detail if you're willing to discover who you truly are. There's a scholars' conference in seven days up north, in the Yorkshire Dales. Send me your email, and I will personally invite you, as I only have one invite left. I look forward to seeing you there and will be your mentor."

Their interaction was a testament to the scholar's character that he was willing to take James under his wing and guide him on his journey towards self-discovery.

And so it was that James found himself on a bus ride to the Yorkshire Dales, filled with anticipation and an open mind. The beauty of the landscape he beheld on his journey was breathtaking, but it was nothing compared to the profound sense of peace he felt upon reaching the village where the conference was being held.

The simplicity of the huts and the spartan living conditions were a far cry from the luxuries he was accustomed to, but it was in this stripped-down environment that he found true serenity. And as he sat among the scholars and listened to their teachings, he knew he was exactly where he was meant to be.

My dear readers, let us not dismiss the words of the scholar as ridiculous or unconventional, for they hold within them the keys to unlocking a deeper understanding of ourselves and the world around us. Let us open our hearts and minds and embrace the journey towards self-discovery, for it is through this journey that we come to know and love ourselves and our fellow beings.

The lecturer began his speech with a gentle and soothing tone, inviting the audience to ponder on the nature of God. Then, he shared insightful ideas about how we are all creatures of the great Creator and how self-realisation leads to the realisation of God. His words were like music to the ears and deeply touched the soul of James, who was experiencing a spiritual awakening.

The lecturer then explained how God desires to have a relationship with us and how our sins, ignorance, and guilt can weaken our connection with Him. Finally, he spoke with wisdom and compassion, inspiring the audience to firmly believe in God and trust that everything that happens in our lives is for a reason.

As James listened intently, the lecturer addressed the concerns of those who had not yet formed a personal relationship with God. He reassured them that they need not do much but simply take the first step by creating a relationship with God through a simple, heartfelt prayer.

"Before going into details of having a good relationship with God, we must first know about God. Who is God according to you?" the scholar said, and there was complete silence in the area.

"We are all the creatures of the great Creator. One thing that has been proven by most laws and philosophy is that creatures possess the qualities of their Creator. Thus, all of us are part of God."

He stopped to take a deep breath before proceeding, "I once read the wonderful book of Rumi, *Forty Rules of Love*. In that book, the author said that what we think about ourselves is the same as what we think about God. So, self-realisation is indeed the realisation of God.

"And now, there are some things that you need to know about God. First, he wanted you to have a relationship with Him. He wanted you to know about Him. That's why, in the Holy Bible, God says, 'So that they should seek the Lord, in the hope that they might grope for Him and find Him, though He is not far from each one of us' (Acts 17:27, KJV).

"And in the Holy Quran, Surah 39:9, 'Allah grant me knowledge of the ultimate nature of things.'"

There was a pin-drop silence; almost everyone wrote essential points on paper or electronic devices. However, the scholar standing in front was casting his spells on the audience with his words and teaching method.

Then he said, "What are the things that can make our relationship worse with God? There is nothing behind disrupting our relationship with God except us. These are our sins, ignorance, and guilt, which can weaken our connection with God."

After taking another breath, he asked the audience, "What do we need to do?"

Looking at the audience, he answered, "We must develop a firm belief in God. To have a healthy relationship with God, we must understand and trust that everything that happens in our lives is for a reason. We must believe that we can better our relationships with ourselves and others simply by strengthening our relationship with God."

Every single word from him seemed as if it were directed towards James. This was because he felt absorbed and mesmerised by the facts he was hearing.

"Some of you might think that you have made the mistake of not having a personal relationship with God or maybe don't have God in your relationships. So, what should be your next step?"

James looked at him as if he was reading his mind and talking directly to him.

"You don't need to do many things to have or begin a relationship with God. Instead, you can begin with today, from this moment. You can start with a simple, heartfelt prayer. You just need to commit yourself by creating a relationship with God. You must take the first step, and then God will take the rest of the steps to maintain that relationship."

The lecturer's words were like honey, sweet and nourishing, leaving a lasting impression on James and the audience. His teaching method was spellbinding, and he cast a spell of positivity and hope on everyone present. As a result, the room was filled with peaceful and serene energy, and James felt blessed to have been part of such a beautiful experience.

Everyone applauded him, and his smile lit up the room as he greeted the learned scholar he had met in London. Then, as the class ended and the others left, James remained seated on the mat, thinking deeply about his relationship with God, pondering what it truly meant.

When night fell, it was a time for meditation and reflection, a chance to connect with oneself and nature. The audience was a diverse mix of people from various religions and cultures seeking self-realisation and spiritual growth. In the morning, the group went for a walk, and the philosophers shared their experiences about the beauty of nature and how it could help them connect with God on a deeper level.

James was amazed at the knowledge and wisdom of the scholars, each one vastly different from the others but all possessing a unique ability to think beyond the ordinary. Spending time with them helped him gain excellent knowledge and spiritual growth, and he was eager to learn more.

"How can I strengthen my relationship with God?" James asked, curious to know the answer.

"As an individual or a couple, the key is to believe in God without hesitation and follow His commands," the scholar replied. "Additionally, being aware of your environment and the beauty of nature can help you connect with God on a deeper level. Just take a moment to look at your surroundings and appreciate the life lessons that can be learned from everything, from the birds in the sky to the trees and the land we inhabit."

The scholar paused momentarily, taking in the peaceful atmosphere around them. "Silence and stillness can be powerful tools in a world filled with negativity and misunderstandings," he continued. "By being silent and avoiding negative comments and gossip, we can strengthen our relationships with others and avoid misunderstandings or miscommunications."

James nodded in agreement, taking in every word of wisdom from the scholars. "And what about our relationship with God?" he asked.

"Our relationship with God is innate; it begins from the moment we are born and lasts until our last breath," the other scholar replied. "It's about including your will in every deed of God or including God in your every action. It's that simple."

James felt his heart fill with warmth and gratitude for the knowledge and wisdom he had gained from the scholars. Walking on the lush green grass, he felt closer to God and more connected to the world around him.

Within a short period, James embarked on a journey of self-discovery that led him to learn from the finest scholars. With great enthusiasm and a sincere heart, he absorbed their teachings. In addition, he observed their behaviours, ultimately developing an effective and heartfelt prayer practice that brought him closer to his divine maker. As a result, he gained valuable insight into his subconscious self. He also received spiritual nourishment from his mentor and fellow scholars, which helped him sense the presence of God in his life and appreciate the beauty of the universe.

James spent an entire month in the company of these enlightened individuals, which was a life-changing experience.

James felt fulfilled and content from this experience despite the steep learning curve and overwhelming information. For the first time in his life, he gained a deep understanding of himself, nature, and God, thanks to the perspectives of various philosophers and religious scholars.

As he packed his bags to return to his hometown of London, James felt a sense of sadness and uncertainty. However, one of the scholars noticed his mood and approached him with words of encouragement. With a reassuring hand on his shoulder, the scholar reminded James that he now possessed the knowledge and power to live a beautiful life no matter where he went. He had learned the importance of integrating God's teachings into his everyday life and the value of living in harmony with nature's laws.

The scholar's words lifted James' spirits, and he felt a newfound strength and resilience. He realised that he had transformed into a different person during his time with the scholars and had the power to face any challenge with grace and poise. With this new perspective, James felt ready to face the same old problems and people back in London with renewed hope and confidence.

With a smile on his face, James recalled all the lectures, group discussions, and counselling sessions that he had participated in, as well as the inner peace and well-being that he had found. He felt grateful for this life-changing experience and vowed to share his newfound wisdom with his friends and loved ones. Thanks to the teachings of the scholars, James had reached a state of self-actualisation that allowed him to live a happy and fulfilling life, no matter where he went.

When he returned to London, he transformed into a new person. Before his spiritual awakening, he was reactive, leading others to keep their distance. This left him to confront his demons and crises alone.

"Who is this person sitting in front of me?" Brian asked playfully, taking note of the serene expression on James' face.

James responded with a smile, radiating the same sense of happiness and inner peace as the scholar that had inspired him.

"James, I see the same happiness and calmness on your face as I did on that scholar's," Brian remarked admiringly.

James beamed with joy. "I've learned to control myself by attending religious conventions and lectures. I've realised that God is always there for me and at the centre of all my actions. These insights have enabled me to cultivate a positive and non-harmful attitude, indirectly beneficial to myself and everyone around me."

"Amazing!" Brian exclaimed in response.

James' life had completely transformed in just a few months. He developed a newfound interest in learning and improving his relationships with his family and friends. Furthermore, he started coaching others at the library on the relationship between God and their inner selves. As a result, his life had taken on an entirely different form and way of living, adding beauty and value to his existence.

James felt blessed and grateful to have God guiding him every step of his life. By remaining in close contact with nature and himself for about six months, constantly learning on YouTube and social media about self-actualisation and discovering the environment in which we live, he found his purpose in life — to serve others.

It was a revelation for his teachers and colleagues to see an introvert deliver lectures on self-realisation. However, his words captivated many people, and students and lecturers alike were curious to hear what he had to say.

He created a Youth Club where he gave lectures on having a relationship with God and discovering one's true inner self. Every Saturday, a group of students would attend his lectures. Every time he stood on stage, he remembered the first time he listened to the scholar who had transformed his life, which motivated him to change others' lives.

One Saturday, while delivering a lecture on believing in the actions and doings of God, he noticed a girl in the audience who appeared to be distressed. After concluding his speech, he approached her and asked, "You don't seem satisfied. Is there something troubling you?"

The girl let out a deep sigh and said, "you're saying that if I believe in the doings of God as the right one, I can live happily. But how can I believe in Him when everything around us brings unhappiness?"

Looking at her with a soft smile, James replied, "I understand your confusion. When I first heard this type of talk, I was just as perplexed as you are now. You see, these are not things you can grasp and implement on yourself by listening to just one lecture. Instead, you must observe and reflect, as observation is the key to understanding anything," James added.

"I see what you mean," the girl replied. "I would love to discuss this further with you."

"Sure, we can meet at Rose Café tomorrow evening. What's your name?" James asked.

"Olivia," she said with a smile.

"Fantastic!" James exclaimed as they bid farewell. After arriving at the hostel, James eagerly delved into his lecture revision. It was the last semester of his MBA degree, and he was thrilled to see his grades improving steadily. His devout approach to every aspect of life had undoubtedly paid off, resulting in exceptional synchronisation between his actions and lifestyle.

The following evening, James eagerly waited for Olivia at the café, smiling brightly as she walked in carrying a bag and file. "I apologise for being late," she said as she sat down.

James responded warmly, "No worries at all!"

As they settled in, Olivia abruptly asked James about his belief that everyone should have faith in God's actions as the best course of action. "James, I'm curious," she began, "what do you mean by saying that we should believe in God's actions as the right or best?"

"Olivia, I'm saying that every event in your life, whether good or bad, is ultimately the right one for you," James explained. "By acknowledging the reasoning behind every action, you will eventually accept it."

Olivia hesitated before finally opening, "Let me give you an example. I was in a relationship for over six months and gave it my all. But one day, I caught my boyfriend with another woman in our bedroom, and he ended things with me. Do you think that was the right thing to happen?"

James calmly poured himself a glass of water and replied, "Absolutely."

Olivia was taken aback, "What do you mean? I gave everything to that relationship, and now you're saying God did the right thing by me?"

James continued, "Yes, I believe God did the right thing by you. You should be grateful that He revealed your boyfriend's character early in the relationship. Perhaps, if he hadn't ended things now, he would have done so in the future, causing you even more pain. Although you may feel hurt now, you will come to see the blessings of this event in time."

Olivia's expression softened as James' sweet words comforted her. "Thank you, James," she said with gratitude. "You always know how to put things in perspective." She was an attentive listener, silently taking in every word James spoke. Even after he finished, she didn't interrupt him but instead reflected on his words. "So, what you're saying is that this was all for the best," she said hushedly.

"Yes, exactly. There are popular sayings that God won't give you more than you can handle and that everything done in the dark will come to light. It's like having faith in God; it gives you the confidence and happiness to know that as long as you do your duty honestly, nothing bad will happen to you. Good will follow your path if you do good things, and bad will follow you if you do bad things," James elaborated.

"Thank you so much for clearing this up for me," she said tearfully. James comforted her with a warm hug before she left. Over the passing days, James and Olivia became closer, bonding over their shared experiences. James was reminded of his debates with the scholars whenever Olivia had questions or challenged a point. One evening, they walked to the library when Olivia turned to James. "James," she called out.

"Yes?" he replied, turning to her.

"What's your idea of the perfect relationship for someone like me? And what should I expect if my boyfriend cheats on me or leaves me?" she asked curiously.

"I don't want to force anyone to believe in God constantly, but if you're doing good in a relationship, you should expect good in return. There's nothing wrong with expecting good things to happen because it commits the universe to be good to you in return. But if you're not getting what you deserve in your current relationship, don't worry because you'll find it elsewhere.

Sometimes the good you do now will follow you into the future and even impact your unborn generations. So never stop being true to yourself and always be honest," he advised.

He paused to breathe and continued, "Also, I don't recommend anyone keep a constant eye on their partners. They have the right to leave anytime, even if you're not married to them. Married couples even fall out of love and get a divorce. What's important is to believe that God won't do you wrong if you're on the right path. He's always there for you; if you have faith and call out to him, he'll be right on time. And if you firmly believe this, God will reward you for it."

"James, you're such an intellectual guy! I feel blessed to have you in my life," Olivia gushed admiringly.

"Thank you," he replied, feeling grateful for their friendship.

As James entered the library, the eager faces of his audience greeted him, and he couldn't help but smile. Then, taking his place on the small stage, he asked the crowd for a topic, and one girl raised her hand with a question that sparked his interest: "How do you add God to a relationship as a couple?"

James knew this was an important topic and wanted to ensure he gave a thoughtful answer. "That's an excellent question," he said, looking at the audience to gauge their interest. "And I think it's something that everyone can benefit from, regardless of your religious beliefs."

As he spoke, his words were like honey to the ears of his listeners, and they hung on every word. "To have a God-centred relationship, it's important to share godly qualities with your partner," he explained, "such as kindness, humility, selflessness, and respect."

James explained that God's love is shown through selflessness, kindness, service, and humility. Therefore, when you involve God in your relationship, you automatically avoid the negativity and toxicity that can harm your relationship. "Having a God-centred relationship benefits you in every way," he continued. "It makes you happier, more present, and more caring when you pray with your partner. And spiritually, it allows you to grow in your life and your relationship with others."

As James finished his talk, the audience was spellbound, and they couldn't help but praise him for his thoughtful and inspiring words. They knew that James was truly blessed with a gift for speaking and were grateful for his guidance and wisdom.

As James looked out at the eager faces in the audience, he felt a deep sense of gratitude for the opportunity to share his wisdom with such an enthusiastic group. When the boy asked for further explanation, James answered with a gentle smile and a warm heart, eager to help this young couple find the path to a deeper connection with each other and with God.

"You're very welcome," James said to the boy, his voice filled with kindness and compassion. "I'm glad I could be of help."

As the applause rang out again, James basked in the glow of the audience's adoration. At that moment, he knew that he had touched the hearts and minds of everyone there and that his message of love, compassion, and connection would continue to inspire them long after he had left the stage.

After nearly a month, James and Olivia sat on a quaint wooden bench, surrounded by the serenity of a beautiful morning breeze that rustled their hair. The fog that lingered in the distance only added to the tranquil ambience. As they sat together, Olivia asked James a thought-provoking question, to which he eagerly replied with his ever-present smile and infectious cheer. No wonder people loved his company; his positive energy was contagious. When Olivia inquired about his opinion on relationships, James turned to face the foggy street and shared his belief that a God-centred marriage was the optimal choice. He spoke with passion and conviction, explaining that a relationship that doesn't lead to marriage is not worth pursuing as it wastes one's precious time and divine energy.

James continued, explaining the power that God has bestowed upon marriage and how a couple who loves God first before each other can experience everlasting love, happiness, and sacrifice. Finally, he stressed the importance of choosing a life partner with care and consideration, as marriage can lead to success and downfall. Later that week, on his resting day, James sat at his study table, opened his diary, and began to write down the valuable lessons and experiences he had learned throughout his spiritual journey. It was a habit he had neglected during his university days, but the recent beautiful months had prompted him to start anew. His diary was filled with regret and complaints in the past, but now it was a record of his growth and gratitude.

Now, he had realised that God was the answer to all his problems. He had seen the light and recognised the beauty of God's doings, services, blessings, selfless love for humankind, and His relationship with every creature in the universe. His perspective had shifted entirely, and he now felt grateful for everything in his life. His diary was filled with pages of gratitude.

Reflecting on his past, James felt a sense of warmth and love fill his heart. Looking back at the pages of his diary, he realised that they were once filled with complaints and grievances towards God. But now, he saw the goodness in everything around him, and his words were filled with sweetness and gratitude.

As the sun began to set, James felt excited and purposeful as he prepared for his evening lecture. He prayed to God for inspiration and felt confident that his prayers were answered. Meeting Olivia on his way to the Youth Club only added to his happiness and sense of fulfilment.

Taking the stage, James felt a sense of calm and confidence wash over him. His words flowed with clarity and conviction, sharing his story of transformation and God's role in his life. His words were like honey, sweet and alluring, captivating the audience's attention and filling them with hope and inspiration.

James spoke about the benefits of having God in our lives, sharing how it had transformed him from a shy and introverted person to a confident and outgoing life coach. He spoke of his struggles, how God had helped him overcome them, and how it changed his life perspective.

The audience was spellbound, their faces reflecting the hope and inspiration that James' words had ignited within them. His message was powerful and uplifting, leaving them feeling blessed and grateful for the gift of God in their lives.

James had found his true calling as a life coach, and his words were like music to the ears of those who heard them. His story was a testament to the power of God and the transformative effect it could have on one's life.

With a gentle pause, James began to speak with the sweetest of tones, "As Master Benaiah finished his lecture, I couldn't help but run towards him, overflowing with excitement to speak with him. At the time, I didn't realise that God had orchestrated that moment for me, but now, I'm grateful for the opportunity that transformed my life. Looking back, I see now that God had been working behind the scenes, putting all the pieces of my life together like a beautiful puzzle. There is no obstacle that God cannot overcome; all we need to do is open our hearts and let His miraculous power work in our lives. When we focus our minds and souls on something, anything is possible, especially when we tap into the gifts that God has given us."

The audience sat transfixed as he spoke, their faces beaming with joy and inspiration. They were captivated by the story of someone who had become a great teacher through the power of God's transformative love.

"After that lecture, I felt a sense of peace and relaxation wash over me. I focused on my studies and prepared for my upcoming exams. His words inspired me to take a chance and attend a religious convention and life coach training. It was a life-changing decision that took me away from my city, friends, and family, but something inside me was calling me to explore myself and my relationship with God. It was a journey that I couldn't ignore."

James paused for a moment to collect his thoughts, and the audience sat spellbound, listening intently to every word.

"When I arrived at my destination, I was greeted by the peaceful stillness of a small village in Yorkshire. There, surrounded by experienced scholars, I learned the art of happiness and how to connect with nature. For the first time, I began to explore who I truly was and discover the beauty of God's creation."

The audience watched with rapt attention as James continued speaking, his voice filled with the sweetest melodies.

"That month changed my life in ways I could never have imagined. It lifted me from the depths of despair and set me on a path towards success and happiness. But, most importantly, it helped me find God and discover my true self."

As James spoke, tears of happiness filled Olivia's eyes, and she rose to her feet to applaud her best friend. The audience joined in; their hearts filled with the sweetness of James' words.

"In a world where stress and pressure abound, it's easy to get caught up in the race to achieve success is easy. But with God in our lives, we can find peace and beauty in even the most mundane moments. So, let me tell you, my friends, that anything is possible when we listen to our hearts and allow God to guide us on our journey."

The audience scribbled furiously on their notepads, eager to capture every word of James' inspiring message. Looking out at the crowd, he couldn't help but smile, remembering the moment that had set him on this incredible journey.

"Having God in your life adds an irreplaceable power that enables you to face life's challenges with a heart full of joy. If you have the presence of God in your life, you can live your life to the fullest. By building a strong relationship with God, you can win the hearts of those around you and find your true purpose in life, just as I did," James said, his voice filled with emotion.

Taking a moment to compose himself, James continued, "I stand here today, in front of all of you, doing something I never thought possible. But through my connection with God, I have discovered my true talents and skills. As the saying goes, 'A person who knows himself is a person who knows God.'

"The benefits of having a strong relationship with God are immeasurable. You will feel a profound change in your life and know that someone is with you every step of the way, protecting you in every situation. That someone is none other than God Himself. Whether you are single or in a relationship, young or old, building a strong relationship with God is essential to living a fulfilled life."

As James concluded his lecture, he left the audience with a final thought: "Education may be the roadmap to success, but the key to success lies in your attitude and in placing God first in your everyday doing. Education is a lifelong process of personal growth and development that can be acquired through formal education or everyday life experiences. So, go out and educate yourself, explore the world, read books, and, most importantly, discover your true potential by building a strong relationship with God."

As the audience rose to applaud James, he wiped away his tears, overwhelmed with emotion. Then, with a smile on his face, he descended from the stage, grateful for the opportunity to share his story and inspire others to find their path in life through their connection with God.

Chapter Three

A Deeper Exploration of Good Intimate Relationships.

This chapter discusses the beginning of an intimate relationship, what to look for in a partner, and the types of Intimacy – physical, spiritual, emotional, and mental. And leave you with questions to ponder about.

Chapter Three

A Deeper Exploration of Good Intimate Relationships

The tears that cry only run dry through forgiveness; forgiveness is the greatest gift for oneself...

*A*midst the frantic commotion, people scurried in search of refuge, their panicked cries echoing through the city. It felt as though the end of days was upon them. Then, standing tall by the sparkling sea, James beheld a sight that left him spellbound; a towering structure emerged from the depths of the blue waters, its prominence visible to all who gazed upon it. As realisation dawned upon him, James shouted to reassure the frightened populace, urging them to remain calm. But no one seemed to heed his words or see what he saw until a resounding voice boomed in his ears.

The entire structure was crafted from exquisite stained glass, resembling those found in the grandest churches. The voice proclaimed, "I am the light, the way, the beginning and the end; heed my words and learn." Each colour in the glass had a significance: green symbolised life, blue represented hope, white denoted purity, yellow signified divinity, and the rainbow is the manifestation of God's presence. James quivered with awe, his legs losing all strength, until he was awoken by a voice calling his name. As he opened his eyes, he realised he had been dreaming, and he fervently prayed, grateful for the gift of such vivid visions.

> *Dreams and Visions are sometimes from GOD. However, He will always make his visions clear to you or send someone who will make them clear to you in due time. Also, be mindful of who you tell your visions to, as some are meant for only you alone. I have learnt from experience. So, again: Be careful about telling people your visions...*

The radiant sun beams caressed the exquisite glass tower of the Youth Club, which now served as James' modest source of income. Two years had passed since he transformed the Ndaha Youth Club into an institute for coaching. Almost every Saturday, the gorgeous building of the Youth Club glittered with profound speeches from the once great teacher, who had evolved into a distinguished scholar. Throughout the weekdays, James and a team of other savants would teach classes to numerous students. The primary goal of establishing this institute had not changed, only that James had transformed his passion into a profession.

Delivering paid lectures to a captivated audience, exploring various aspects of life's dilemmas with fellow scholars, and discovering solutions to the complexities of life and relationships were all utterly enthralling for James.

Bathed in the warm glow of the morning sun, the radiant James had become an altruistic beacon of hope for his community. He had spent countless hours in pursuit of wisdom and knowledge, becoming a veritable sage and mentor to all who sought his guidance. Despite facing numerous challenges in recent times, from attending various religious conventions across Europe and Asia to overcoming personal struggles, he remained steadfast in his faith, applying the teachings of God to his daily life. Through his tireless efforts, he had even managed to raise over half a million pounds to establish a youth centre for the betterment of his community. One serene morning, James was immersed in deep meditation, seated on a pristine white rug amidst a bevy of blooming flowerpots. Meanwhile, Olivia, whom James had aided in launching a bustling breakfast restaurant, attempted to reach him via phone. However, James was so focused on the spiritual practice that he could not hear Olivia's call, as his voice was hushed and subdued.

Olivia left a sweet message for James, asking to meet up after he finished his prayer and meditation. James eagerly replied, promising to meet her at noon. Olivia held a special place in James' heart, and their friendship grew stronger daily. Despite her obvious attraction towards him, James maintained a professional and respectful demeanour around her, always careful not to overstep any boundaries. As Olivia arrived, James couldn't help but notice the sparkle in her eyes, the hopefulness in her expression, and the warmth of her smile. When they hugged, James felt a current of electricity pass through his body, and he knew instantly that Olivia was the missing piece in his life. With a gentle touch, Olivia asked the question on her mind. "Is marriage still worth it in our generation?" she wondered aloud.

"Marriage is a divine union between two souls, a sacred bond that connects two hearts together in a meaningful and fulfilling way. It can bring joy, love, and prosperity into your life and help you grow and evolve as a person. It's not just a legal contract but a deep commitment to each other that can withstand the tests of time and challenges of life. While some may argue that marriage is outdated, I believe a strong and healthy marriage can be a source of great happiness and fulfilment. However, it's important to choose your partner carefully and ensure that you share a strong bond of friendship and mutual respect. Good communication is also crucial for a successful marriage, as it can help prevent misunderstandings and conflicts from escalating. Ultimately, the decision to marry or not is a personal one that should be based on your values, beliefs, and feelings," James explained.

"So, suppose you strongly connect with someone and believe they are the one for you?" Olivia asked the question politely.

"In that case, marriage can be a wonderful journey that will bring you closer together and enrich your lives in countless ways," James replied, gazing into Olivia's captivating eyes.

"So, you mean marriage is better than an unnamed relationship?" Olivia gazed at James with a heart full of passion and curiosity. Her eyes reflected her love and emotion for him, and she couldn't wait to hear his response.

James smiled softly, nodding his head as he spoke gently. "Marriage is a divine union that allows us to experience the purest form of love. It's a bond created by God and teaches us to love selflessly, just like how God loves us all. Through marriage, two people become one, connected by a spiritual bond that lasts a lifetime. It's a beautiful journey that makes life more meaningful and fulfilling."

As James finished his words, Olivia took a deep breath, her heart racing with excitement. "Alright," she said, unable to contain her joy, "tell me when you're going to marry me!" Her swift response took James aback, but a wide grin spread across his face, and his eyes sparkled with happiness. Olivia smiled back, feeling the warmth of his love wash over her.

"You're so quick," he chuckled, and Olivia's gaze fixed on his face.

"But that's not the answer to my question," she said, her voice filled with eagerness.

James took a moment to gather his thoughts before responding. "Very soon," he said, his tone full of conviction. "Let me be the one to propose to you in a beautiful setting, with a ring fit for a woman of your calibre." Olivia laughed at his words, and James couldn't help but join her. The morning had become even

THE ASPECT OF RELATIONSHIPS

more enchanting, and they both felt grateful for each other's company. After attending counselling sessions, James eventually proposed, and they exchanged vows in a beautiful ceremony, surrounded by their loved ones.

After four wonderful years of marriage, James sat in his cosy room, admiring the peaceful drizzle outside. The enchanting scenery outside was a balm to his soul, and he relished this moment of tranquillity. James had recently completed his PhD in Theology and was now working at a well-paying job while managing the youth centre he had established. He was enjoying the most delightful phase of his married life with Olivia, and God had blessed them with a beautiful daughter…

Suddenly, he heard the soft pitter-patter of footsteps approaching him. Without opening his eyes, he already knew who it was — his adorable four-year-old daughter, Emma, taking small steps towards him. But his eyes were still closed. "I won't disturb you, Daddy," Emma whispered into his ear sweetly. James couldn't help but smile at his daughter's adorable antics. Finally, he opened his eyes and saw that she had sat beside him in the same pose. Her hair was uncombed, and James knew she had just woken up. He looked at her, and seeing her innocence, he couldn't resist kissing her forehead. But his daughter made a face and said, "You are disturbing me, Daddy!" James couldn't help but chuckle at her response. Emma then stood up and looked at him with an angry face.

"Alright, alright!" James held her tiny hands and said, "Do you want Daddy to teach you how to meditate?"

Emma's beautiful green eyes sparkled with excitement, "Yes," she replied eagerly.

"Okay, first, go and get your mom's rug. Later, I'll buy one for you," James instructed her. Emma ran towards the cupboard and picked up Olivia's rug, which was too big for her hands,

James reached out to help her, but she refused. James looked at her, smiling. He loved spending time with her. "Now, you have to sit down," James said, spreading the mat on the floor. "Close your eyes and count your breaths," he said, sitting in front of her.

Spending time with your children is the best gift from God and very refreshing, he thought, looking at her...

The morning was tranquil as the students of the Youth Club gathered in the main hall for their daily meditation. The air was crisp, and the windows were wide open, allowing the refreshing breeze from the garden to enter and soothe their souls. The students sat on their yoga mats and rugs, taking deep breaths and clearing their minds of all thoughts. The silence in the hall was absolute, with only the sound of their breaths filling the space. Once the meditation was over, the students dispersed to their respective classes. Coach Robert took this opportunity to talk to them about the importance of self-help books, holding up Leil Lowndes' *How to instantly connect with Anyone* as an example. "Today, your task is to read the first chapter of this book," Master Robert instructed. "Tomorrow, we'll discuss what we've learned from it as a class." The Youth Club was an inclusive space, welcoming students of all ages, backgrounds, and beliefs to come and learn how to find peace and meaning in their lives. The students settled into different groups doing activities, Master Robert said, "Today, Master James will deliver a lecture on 'Finding a soulmate in life.'"

In the mid-afternoon, James sat in his study room, surrounded by books about love, relationships, and finding love. He pondered over his notes, crafting each word for his upcoming lecture. Then, finally, he took a fresh sheet of paper, uncapped his pen, and jotted down the most crucial points. As the evening sun set, James arrived at the Youth Club, accompanied by Olivia and Emma...

The entire hall was brimming with eager faces waiting for him. Finally, he stepped onto the stage, and applause filled the air. James looked at the audience, beaming from ear to ear, and expressed his gratitude to God. He lifted the mic, waved to the crowd, and with a smile, greeted them, "Good evening, everyone!" His topic for the day was 'Finding a soulmate in life,' and he was excited to share his wisdom. James acknowledged that talking about relationships and soulmates might make some people uncomfortable. But he appreciated the audience's decision to attend the lecture, knowing that learning about love and finding the one is essential for everyone. He began his talk with the question, "What is a soulmate?" James engaged and captivated the audience throughout the lecture with his unmatched style and charisma.

As he paused, the air was filled with anticipation, waiting for the following words to escape his lips. Finally, with a soft smile, he spoke again, "When it comes to the definition of a soulmate, countless interpretations exist, each more beautiful than the last. But my personal favourite, which I believe in wholeheartedly, comes from the beloved American drama series *Dawson's Creek.*" The audience leaned in, their eyes bright and eager, some nodding in agreement as they remembered the show. "A soulmate is like a best friend, but better," he recited. "It's that one person in the world who knows you better than anyone else. Someone who brings out the best in you and inspires you to be your most authentic self. They don't make you a better person, you do that yourself, but they support and encourage you every step of the way." The room was peaceful, and all ears focused on James' advice.

"A soulmate is someone you can carry with you forever," he continued. "It's the person who accepts, believes and knows you, even when no one else does. And no matter what life throws your way, you'll always love them unconditionally." A ripple of applause filled the hall as the crowd absorbed the heartfelt words. "But…" James paused, a sly grin spreading across his face. "I know what many of you are thinking now, 'Finding a soulmate is impossible!' Well, believe me when I say I used to think the same thing until I met my soulmate, Olivia," he gestured to the young woman sitting in the front row, her face radiant with love and happiness.

"A lot of people ask me what qualities they should look for in a partner or when finding a soulmate. Firstly, from my point of view, it can't be defined by naming some characteristics because everyone has a changed perspective on a partner. Secondly, you may have heard that one should seek honesty, kindness, a nice personality, or character in a partner. I agree with that. Surely these are the main things that play a significant role in building any relationship. But..." James stopped for a moment. "The thing that I prefer is the spirituality and openness of an individual." He took a deep breath and added, "By spirituality, I don't mean the one who goes to church or mosque daily. Instead, spirituality is the root of a nice character. For example, a grateful person is also spiritual. A person who prefers listening to you. A person who is excellent in all types of relationships. Such as the relationships with parents, friends, teachers, and every creature of the universe." There was a satisfying silence in the hall.

Every eye was on him and concentrating on his face, absorbing every word from his mouth. "People who go to church and mosque every day are building a relationship with the great creator, and the majority of them are not spiritual even though they sometimes portray themselves as the holiest of holies. Openness is the key characteristic of a partner. It is also an acronym for acceptance. You, as a partner, should be open to expressing your feelings. It means that a person should be kind enough to accept you as you are without forcing or implementing his criteria on you," James said.

"Listen to me carefully..." He could see the focus of all his students towards him. "Having a perfect person with all your desired traits is impossible. Because God is not a genie in the lamp, to whom you say, 'I need a person with these qualities,' rubbing the lamp and that person will appear in front of you with all the things you desired in your partner. And then, you'll later say, 'No, that one is not according to my desire and liking. Give me a new one,' and God will replace them with a new one. Don't we all wish life was like that!'" James smiled.

The hall erupted with the sweet sound of laughter once again, filling the room with a joyful ambience. "Let's all keep this in mind," James continued, looking out to the eager audience. "You must also make yourself the best version to attract your desired partner. I firmly believe in the *Law of Attraction*, which suggests that you attract what you put out into the world. So, cultivate the qualities you seek in a partner within yourself." The audience nodded in agreement as they listened to James' wise words. "In addition, finding a partner whose core values align with yours is crucial. This is the cornerstone of any successful relationship, and it's what makes a partner your soulmate. When you share the same values and perspectives on life, you can truly enjoy the joy and beauty of a genuine connection." James' words were met with admiration and awe, with the audience eagerly jotting down notes on their notepads. His confidence on stage grew as he continued to speak.

James continued to share his wisdom with the audience, his words flowing effortlessly like honey. "If you are struggling to identify the qualities you want in a partner, fear not. Another important factor you need to focus on is emotional maturity. This is a key characteristic that every successful relationship needs, as it allows you to navigate difficult situations with ease and take responsibility for your feelings and actions. Reactive behaviour will only lead to more problems down the road." The audience was hanging on every word James spoke, their eyes glistening with interest and intrigue. "Now, here's the answer to a question on everyone's mind, 'How do you begin an intimate relationship?' It's simple," James said, walking closer to the audience. "By understanding what qualities, you want in a partner and developing those qualities yourself, you'll be better equipped to start a relationship with a soulmate. Sharing the same core values and interests creates a solid foundation for a meaningful relationship."

James paused for a moment, catching his breath before continuing. "But before you start looking for someone else to fill the void in your life, it's important to remember that relationships are not meant to complete you. You need to work on yourself and understand your subconscious and conscious self before truly understanding and connecting with another person."

The audience nodded in agreement, their pens scribbling furiously on their notepads as they absorbed every word of James' speech. James' voice was soothing and enchanting as he continued to speak, "When embarking on a relationship, focusing on self-improvement is vital. This means that you need to bring something of value to the table. Relationships aren't just about receiving; they're about mutual growth and connection. It's about sharing your beliefs and ideas without imposing them on your partner. Relationships transform sickness into health, poverty into wealth," James proclaimed with conviction. He explained that creating enough space in your mind to accept your partner's opinions, thoughts, and shortcomings when starting an intimate relationship is essential. "When you accept them as they are, flaws and all, you show them the utmost importance in the relationship, which creates an incredible bond."

"Pride can be a relationship killer," James warned. Although not all pride is negative, excessive pride can be detrimental. "Pride comes before the fall," he said. "Some people are convinced they're always right and rarely apologise for their mistakes. They can be arrogant and self-centred, causing communication and connection to suffer. Pride can be a destructive force, ruining people's talents and dreams. It's crucial to be humble and kind, at peace with yourself and others, and to make amends for past mistakes. Most importantly, work on yourself."

Moreover, as James looked out at the eager faces in the audience, he began to speak about the unfortunate reality of the current pandemic's impact on relationships. "During the pandemic, we've seen countless cases of breakups and separations among partners," he said, his voice filled with empathy. "Researchers have discovered that the number one reason behind this is the lack of time or communication in a relationship." He explained that when one neglects to spend quality time with their partner, it can lead to feelings of insignificance and rejection that are detrimental to any relationship.

Stepping back towards the centre of the stage, James continued with some sage advice from Helene Brenner's book, *I Know I'm In There Somewhere*. According to her, true intimacy involves giving each other undivided attention and creating a special connection. "If you want to feel close to your partner, you need to put away distractions and truly focus on each other," he said.

In conclusion, James left the audience with a powerful message: "To attract the perfect partner in your life, you must first become the best version of yourself. Then, the universe will match you with someone who possesses the same qualities you have developed in yourself." He smiled as the audience gave him a standing ovation. It was a moment of pride and contentment for James, knowing that he had contributed to the betterment of humanity by spreading positivity and love through his words...

James was excited as he packed his suitcase for the upcoming Mega Week Event in Atlanta. His wife, Olivia, and their daughter, Emma, joined him on this intellectual trip with a much-needed vacation. James carefully placed his diary and pen in the luggage and went to the living room, where Olivia and Emma were already packing Emma's lovely dresses and shoes. As soon as Emma saw her dad, she ran towards him with a wide smile, showing off her beautiful dress and shoes. James scooped up his little girl, lifting her onto his shoulder easily. "Are you ready?" he asked with a smile. Emma nodded eagerly, her hazel eyes sparkling with excitement.

The journey from London to Atlanta was long, but they finally arrived to be welcomed by the extreme heatwave of the vibrant city. James had planned the short trip as a surprise for Olivia and Emma, making all the arrangements without their knowledge. The main topic of discussion at the Mega Week

Event was intimacy in relationships, a subject close to James' heart. The event lasted four days, with all activities and events listed in the program and flyers. When the event concluded, James could enjoy the remaining days with his family in one of the most visited and expensive cities in the United States.

With excitement and wonder in her eyes, Emma revelled in every moment of their first family trip. James, determined to make it memorable, took them to Georgia Aquarium and World of Coca-Cola on their first day in Atlanta. They stopped at Centennial Olympic Park on their way back to their apartment. Emma's joy knew no bounds as she shouted excitedly while trying out every slide and swing, she could find. James was overjoyed seeing his daughter so happy, but he couldn't help but feel a tinge of guilt. He realised he had been so caught up with work and lectures that he had never taken Emma on outdoor adventures. It was a new experience for her, and he wished he had done it sooner. Olivia noticed Emma's love for outdoor activities and remarked it to James. Emma's happiness was infectious, and the couple couldn't help but smile at their daughter's delight. But James knew he had to make it up to her and give her more opportunities to have fun and experience the world around her. After their time at the park, they returned to their apartment, and James sat at his study table, reflecting on the day's events. He couldn't wait to make more memories with his family in the beautiful city of Atlanta.

Today, James was hit with a realisation that left him feeling sorrowful. As a parent, he had unknowingly done his daughter wrong. Although, despite his good intentions of providing her with spiritual education from a young age, he had inadvertently taken away her childhood by always bringing her to his lectures and addresses. After they visited Centennial Park, he genuinely realised the extent of his error.

Emma's joyful laughter and carefree spirit, as she played with other children around her, opened his eyes to the fact that he had denied her the chance to experience the simple pleasures of childhood. James paused his pen as he gazed upon a picture of Emma on the coffee table, feeling regretful for not giving her a chance to enjoy her childhood. He wiped away his tears with a tissue, then began writing again. "It is a love of Storge," a Greek word he wrote, "a natural, unconditional love that exists between parents and children." As he reminisced on precious memories of Emma's first steps, her first words, and their first cooking experience together, his heart overflowed with love for his daughter.

With a contented smile on his face, James continued to pour his heart out onto the paper. Like a gentle stream, his pen flowed smoothly as he expressed his newfound appreciation for his daughter and the importance of nurturing her childhood.

'Watching Emma play at Centennial Park today, I realised that childhood is a magical time that should be cherished and enjoyed to the fullest. It's a time when everything is new and exciting, and children are filled with wonder and joy. As parents, it's our responsibility to provide them with a safe and nurturing environment where they can explore and learn at their own pace. I understand now that my desire to teach Emma about spirituality and leadership was well-intentioned but misguided. I was so focused on preparing her for the future that I forgot to enjoy the present moment with her. I was trying to mould her into something she may not have been ready for instead of allowing her to be the free-spirited, curious child she is.

'But now, I see that my daughter's happiness and well-being are paramount. I vow to create a childhood full of fun, laughter, and love. I want to be there for her, to play and explore alongside her, and to witness her growth and development with wonder and pride. I'm grateful for this awakening, for the opportunity to correct my parenting course and provide my daughter with the nurturing environment she deserves. As I close my diary for the night, I feel a sense of peace and contentment, knowing that I'm on the right path to being the best parent I can be.' James breathed in deeply, gazing upon the words he had penned with a sense of satisfaction. He carefully closed his diary and approached his daughter's bed, where she laid sleeping. Bending down, he pressed a tender kiss onto her forehead and whispered, "I love you, Emma," feeling an overwhelming sense of contentment washing over him as he did so.

As Emma stirred awake the following day, she found her parents sitting at her bedside. James had shared his thoughts on parenting with Olivia, and after reading his diary, she saw the truth in his words. "You're right, James. There's something vital missing in our parenting that's critical to her growth," Olivia said, looking at their daughter with a newfound awareness. Then, with a renewed determination to foster their daughter's growth, they set out for their morning walk in the park; this time, they visited Atlanta Botanical Garden and Piedmont Park. Olivia's words about the park filled Emma's eyes with delight, and she bounced up and down with excitement. James and Olivia exchanged a knowing smile as they watched their daughter play and laugh with abandon. Seeing their child so happy was the greatest joy that they could experience as parents…

In the enchanting evening, they found themselves in the grandest hall of Atlanta. James gently removed his paper pad and pen while sitting in the second row with his beloved Olivia and Emma. The Mega Event they attended invited four distinguished scholars to lecture on the various forms of Intimacy in relationships. The first lecture was on 'Emotional Intimacy in Relationships' by the renowned Master Benaiah.

As if by magic, Master Benaiah appeared on stage, with a serene and divine face, just like the first time James had seen him five years ago on a small stage in London. His warm smile and welcoming demeanour put one's mind at ease, and it was as if time had stood still. For a moment, James was transported back to his past, where he remembered attending Master Benaiah's lecture during one of the darkest periods of his life and how his words and teachings had transformed him into a new person.

As the claps from the audience died down, Master Benaiah greeted them casually and humbly, "Welcome, everybody! It's my great privilege and honour to stand on this magnificent platform before you." James couldn't help but smile at the sight of Master

Benaiah on stage. His words were spellbinding, as he spoke with utmost sincerity and selflessness, making everyone feel at home.

As the audience listened intently, Master Benaiah's words flowed like honey, sweet and comforting to the soul. His gentle voice was like a warm embrace, inviting everyone to open their hearts and minds to his teachings. "Today's lecture is all about Emotional Intimacy in relationships," he began, his words dripping with kindness. "But before we dive into that, let us first understand what intimacy truly means. When we think of intimacy, our minds often jump to thoughts of physical touch and sexual activity. But intimacy is so much more than that." He paused, letting his words sink in, before continuing, "Intimacy is the feeling of closeness and connection between two individuals. The soothing comfort comes from being with someone who truly understands and accepts you for who you are."

The audience was completely enraptured by his words, nodding along in agreement. "As I'm sure you're all aware, there are four major types of intimacy in relationships: emotional, spiritual, mental, and physical. Each type plays a crucial role in the success and sustainability of a relationship." He smiled, his eyes twinkling with warmth. "While I'm here to specifically discuss emotional intimacy today, I want to emphasise that all types of intimacy are equally important."

Sitting in the second row with Olivia and Emma, James couldn't help but feel grateful for the wisdom Master Benaiah was imparting.

"Emotional intimacy is about connecting with your partner on a deep emotional level. It involves expressing your feelings, vulnerabilities, trust and allowing yourself to be truly seen and understood by your partner. It's the highest level of connection between two individuals, sharing the same interests, sense of humour, and outlook on life." Master Benaiah's words were like a gentle breeze, carrying everyone away to a world of love, trust, and understanding. The audience was left feeling inspired and hopeful, ready to practice his teachings in their relationships.

Master Benaiah spoke with a tender voice that captured the hearts of his audience. He said, "Emotional intimacy is a sanctuary where couples share their deepest feelings and thoughts with each another. It is the foundation of a relationship that withstands any storm. It nurtures the growth of love, trust, and mutual understanding, which are essential ingredients for a happy and healthy relationship." He paused for a moment to let his words sink in before continuing, "Without emotional intimacy, a relationship is like a garden without water. It will wither and die. The lack of emotional intimacy is a leading cause of divorce worldwide. The invisible enemy creeps into a relationship and tears it apart."

Master Benaiah's eyes met the gaze of his audience, and he said, "But it doesn't have to be that way. Emotional intimacy is the key to a successful and lasting relationship. It has the power to transform weaknesses into strengths and challenges into opportunities. When two people share their vulnerabilities and trust one another, they create an unbreakable bond that can conquer any obstacle." He took a deep breath and continued, "Emotional intimacy strengthens a relationship and affects every aspect of a couple's life. It helps them face challenges together, overcome stress and adversity, and become each other's rock. When a couple has emotional intimacy, they are a team that no opponent can defeat."

Master Benaiah's words were like honey, sweet and soothing to the ears. His message was clear: emotional intimacy is the heart of a relationship; without it, a relationship cannot survive. Not only is it my belief, but Rachel Wright, a marriage counsellor and psychotherapist, also shares that a lack of emotional intimacy can lead to feelings of insecurity, lack of love and support, and disconnection in relationships, which ultimately affects physical intimacy. Such a relationship cannot be sustained long-term, and it is crucial to understand the significance of emotional intimacy in establishing a successful and fulfilling relationship.

As Master Benaiah addressed the audience, his words were laced with a sweet and honeyed touch, encouraging them to nurture their relationships. He explained that developing emotional intimacy is the key to a happy and progressive life with a partner. "Let me show you the way," he said with a smile, drawing the eager attention of the audience. "The first and foremost thing you must do is start giving time to your partner," he said. "Time is a valuable gift that strengthens your bond and allows you to connect on a deeper level. Take moments out of your busy schedule to share activities such as watching a movie or cooking together. These small acts may seem trivial, but they work wonders in enhancing your relationship."

Master Benaiah's voice was soothing and reassuring as he continued, "Daily compliments and affirmations are the second things that improve emotional intimacy in relationships. Recognising and appreciating your partner's actions create an environment of positivity and mutual admiration. As a result, your partner will feel appreciated and valued, and this will strengthen the emotional bond between you."

The audience hung onto every word, captivated by how Master Benaiah's words flowed like molten gold. He spoke with such eloquence and conviction, his message resonating with them deeply. They were engrossed in Master Benaiah's talk. Master Benaiah continued speaking, "It means that you should tell your partner how much they matter to you, how deeply you love them, and keep them aware of any issue you are dealing with. If you avoid discussing an issue that needs to be discussed only because you are afraid of your partner's bad temper, you are doing something wrong. In that way, you are minimising the sphere of understanding from your relationship."

As the lecture timing ended, Master Benaiah concluded the lecture with a smile, "In conclusion, only you can save your relationship. No one else is going to do it for you. So, no matter your relationship, you can save and restore your relationships by considering all the points I have discussed."

The hall echoed with applause, except for James, who was still sitting quietly, looking as if his soul had been extracted. Perhaps this trip to Atlanta was for assessing James' role in life. Master Benaiah's words had just lost him. Olivia asked, "Shall we go?" looking at James, who stood up without a word and walked out of the hall. He was quiet on the way back home, lost in thought. Although Olivia noticed his silence, she didn't want to intrude, thinking Master Benaiah's lecture probably inspired James or he couldn't control himself after seeing his mentor.

Back at his apartment, James had dinner and went to the study table. He opened his diary. Emma's and Olivia's pictures were placed on the table. His mind started aching. He was thinking about his relationships with his family members. Today, he wasn't going to write about the points of Master Benaiah's lecture on emotional intimacy in relationships. Instead, he was analysing his life and relationships.

With his trusty black pen in hand, James inscribed on the top of the page of his diary, 'What manner of relationships do I have with my beloved spouse?' The room was filled with complete silence, save for the soft breathing of his sleeping family members on the bed. Then, turning towards his diary, James began to write. 'I'm not quite certain what is occurring in my life. Before attending these lectures in Atlanta, I believed I was doing my utmost in my relationships. However, this brief trip has opened my eyes and revealed how well or poorly I am faring in my relationships.'

James paused, taking a deep breath to steady his emotions. 'One thing I now realise is that the learning process is never-ending. Regardless of how much education or knowledge one acquires about life or finances, we can never fully know everything. The same holds for me. If I reflect upon the past, things were different from when I first met Olivia until our marriage. I distinctly remember that before our weddings, we spend ample time together, discussing various topics and sharing opinions on different life perspectives. We used to talk about how to improve our relationship as friends.' His hands halted once more as he was overcome with emotion. In his lectures, James frequently urged couples to make time for each other, but he was oblivious that he needed to spend more time with his family. Recalling all those memories was an arduous task.

'My life has taken an unexpected turn, and I struggle to understand my relationships. I had convinced myself I was doing my best before coming to Atlanta for Master Benaiah's lecture series. However, this short trip has opened my eyes to the reality of my situation. It has shown me how well or poorly I am doing in my relationships.' James paused and took a deep breath, his thoughts racing. 'One thing has become clear: the learning journey is never-ending. No matter how much knowledge one acquires, there will always be more to learn. This trip has made me realise that things were different in the past. When I first met Olivia, we spent so much time together, discussing various topics and sharing our perspectives on life. We were friends, and we discussed the importance of building strong relationships before getting married.' James took a moment to reflect before continuing to write. 'I can't help but feel a sense of guilt as I realise that I have not been practising what I preach. In my lectures, I encourage couples to spend time with each other, but I have been neglecting my own family. Recalling all the memories is difficult, but I know we have not spent enough time together.' James paused again, deep in thought.

'Master Benaiah's lecture was a test for me, a way to assess my relationship score. And the reality is that our relationship lacks emotional intimacy, mainly due to our busy schedules. I know I am at fault, spending most of my time at the Youth Club. However, Olivia also has her responsibilities, running her restaurant and taking care of Emma. As a result, we have spent less and less time together since Emma's birth. It's a red flag in any relationship when couples don't spend time together.' James looked over at his beloved Olivia, sound asleep on the bed. 'Today, I have gained a deeper understanding of the different kinds of love that exist in our lives. Love evolves and changes over time, depending on our age and life experiences. When I first met Olivia, our love was playful and uncommitted. We were best friends, sharing questions and opinions with each other. At that time, Olivia was in the first stage of Mania love, and although I was unaware of it, I could sense her importance in my life.

'But with time, we entered the Eros love just before our marriage. Like any other couple, We shared romantic and intimate moments. After we married, our love changed from Eros to Pragma — a mature love between husband and wife. This is not just my story; almost all married couples have the same story. They also talk about the decrease in their post-marriage relationship, which is very different from their expectations before getting married.'

James cast a fond gaze at the photograph of his beloved Olivia that sat on the nearby table. Grateful to have opened his eyes to the importance of nurturing his relationships, he thanked the heavens above for granting him the wisdom to work on his bond with his wife and daughter. Olivia had never complained about their lack of intimacy; her gentle and generous nature had always put James at ease. Now, determined to reignite the spark between them, James closed his pen and took a deep, contented breath.

The following day, James rose from bed a little later than usual and found Olivia dutifully serving breakfast to Emma. Admiring the two most important women in his life, he headed to the bathroom for a refreshing shower. When he emerged, Olivia was ready for her morning walk, and Emma was all dressed up and ready to go. With a smile of pure joy on his face, James savoured this moment, grateful for the love and companionship of his dear family.

"Are you ready to climb Stone Mountain today, my loves?" James asked, his voice gentle and sweet.

Emma squealed with delight, "Yes, Daddy!" He chuckled and lifted her onto his shoulders, making her giggle even more.

"Before we go, I have a little secret to share," he said, lowering his voice to a whisper.

Emma's eyes widened with curiosity, "What is it, Daddy?"

"Look at Mommy; she looks so pretty today, doesn't she?" he said, his gaze fixed on Olivia. Olivia's heart fluttered at the unexpected compliment and blushed with pleasure.

Emma eagerly agreed, "Yes, Mommy looks beautiful!"

As they walked to Stone Mountain Park before climbing the Mountain, Emma ran off to play, leaving James and Olivia alone on the bench. Olivia turned to him, and her heart was full of warmth and love. James smiled at her, "I just wanted to say I love you," he said softly. Olivia was caught off guard by his words and couldn't help but laugh joyfully. Tears filled her eyes, and she quickly wiped them away. James looked concerned, "What's wrong, Olivia?"

She shook her head, "Nothing, it's just...I'm so happy," she said, beaming at him.

He reached for her hand, "I love you too," he said, his voice filled with sincerity. Her eyes sparkled with joy, and she leaned in for a gentle hug. As they embraced, their love for each other filled their hearts, and they knew that they would always work to keep their marriage strong and full of love.

They forwent the lecture that day, and instead, James took his beloved family to various sightseeing activities to relish more time together. As James nestled into bed that night, a sense of ideal contentment washed over him, buoyed by the knowledge that he had played his best role in fostering his family relationships. Once again, his countenance lit up with a beaming smile.

On the event's third day, James found himself seated in the main hall once more alongside Olivia and Emma. The day's topic was Mental and Physical Intimacy in relationships, and the family sat together in the second row, attentively listening to the speaker. As Dr William took the stage, he greeted the audience warmly, "Good Evening, everyone!" he announced, his voice carrying through the hall. "Today's discussion focuses on the relationship between mental and physical intimacy in relationships. In our materialistic and self-centred society, mental intimacy is often neglected, and physical intimacy is viewed as the sole measure of love and commitment. However, this is a misconception that we must correct. The current state of family crises underscores the need for this important conversation about intimacy."

Dr William paused, surveying the audience before him. "Indeed, maintaining true mental intimacy can be challenging in our current society. Our modern generation often views mental intimacy as an outdated strategy for love. However, this is far from the truth," he continued, his gaze still fixed on the crowd.

"I understand that cultivating true mental intimacy in our relationships can be challenging in today's world. Our communal lifestyle significantly impacts our ability to develop and maintain mental intimacy. We now live in the 21st century, where social media reigns supreme, and a person's online presence is often more critical than physical interaction. With platforms such as Facebook, WhatsApp, Twitter, Instagram, TikTok, and Snapchat dominating our lives, we have become a social media generation.

Unfortunately, many individuals today are more concerned with obtaining likes and validation, even if it means ignoring those around them. This trend can lead to misconceptions about what real intimacy entails, leading to relationship breakdowns. If not managed appropriately, social media can also influence our thoughts and decisions in ways that may be detrimental to our relationships."

The room fell into a hushed and contemplative silence as Dr William's words penetrated deep into the hearts of those present. His soothing voice filled the hall, carrying with it a message of hope and wisdom that resonated with everyone. "It is a sad truth that we have become a society obsessed with physical interaction, to the point where we have forgotten the importance of mental intimacy in our relationships," he lamented, his eyes scanning the audience with empathy. "Our culture has instilled in us the belief that the foundation of a healthy relationship lies solely in physical contact. But this is a misguided notion that has led to many broken marriages and shattered hearts. We must relearn the value of mental intimacy, which is the key to building lasting relationships," Dr William explained, his voice infused with passion and conviction.

He continued, "Mental intimacy is more than just spending time with your partner. It is about truly connecting with them, understanding them on a deep level, and respecting their feelings and opinions. It is about creating a safe space where you can share your innermost thoughts, fears, and dreams without fear of judgment or rejection." He then turned to James and smiled,

"And as Master James once said, mental intimacy is the quality that enables you to listen to your partner's opinion about a specific thing without clashing or arguing. It is a rare and precious gift that we must strive to cultivate in our relationships." The room erupted into applause as everyone felt inspired by Dr William's words. James felt a sense of pride and gratitude wash over him, knowing he had played a small part in spreading this message of love and connection.

Dr William's words left the audience deep in thought. They were in awe of his wisdom and knowledge. His words were like a refreshing breeze in the suffocating atmosphere of a society that overvalues physical intimacy. His words were like a light in the darkness of the modern era that is losing touch with human connection.

The audience could feel the passion in Dr William's voice when he talked about mental intimacy. They could feel his warmth and love for his partner when he spoke about their mental association. They could feel the joy he had experienced when their opinions matched. They could feel the essence of his love for his partner. They realised that mental intimacy is the language of love that creates a strong bond between partners.

Dr William's words were like a wake-up call for the audience. They realised they had been neglecting mental intimacy in their relationships and needed to change that. They realised that they needed to prioritise mental intimacy over physical intimacy to create a long-lasting, healthy relationship.

Dr William's words were like a seed that would grow into a tree of love and connection. The seed would blossom into a beautiful relationship between partners. The seed would bring joy and happiness into their lives.

As Dr William gazed at the audience, he spoke passionately, "As we come to the end of this lecture, let us remember that the four types of intimacy are essential in any relationship. It's more than just knowing yourself and having feelings for another; it's about a deep connection, excitement, and the giving and receiving of pleasure and closeness. All of which are essential for human beings and should be balanced with the presence of God in our relationships."

The audience rose to their feet, clapping in appreciation for the insightful lecture. James couldn't help but smile as he left the lecture hall that day, feeling grateful for the wisdom he had gained in improving and growing his relationship with Olivia.

Upon returning home that night, James felt renewed motivation to improve his relationships with his family, determined to play his best role in strengthening those bonds. As he sat on the bed with Olivia and Emma, they shared stories and thoughts with each other, and James felt the joy and beauty of a family relationship.

On the final day of the Mega Event, James was eager to attend the lecture on spiritual intimacy in relationships. His love for spirituality and desire to deepen his connection with God made it a must-attend event. Despite being late and missing the start, James and his family were excited to be there, sitting in the middle of the audience, ready to absorb all the wisdom they could.

Master Brown, a renowned scholar, captivated the audience with his lecture from the centre stage.

"Spirituality is the art of profoundly connecting the core of your being to each other while preserving yourself. It is a mutual experience of closeness with God through our relationships. This mutual spiritual connection creates a powerful and profound emotional and physical bond with one another, unlike anything else. Before establishing a spiritual relationship with your partner, you must have a spiritual relationship with God and yourself. Someone who thinks too highly of themselves cannot be in a spiritual relationship with someone else because, in a spiritual relationship, two hearts are joined together by God without knowing why," Master Brown spoke.

"Spirituality is unbeatable in relationships. It does not necessarily mean a strictly religious interaction but rather an experience of total harmony, understanding, peace and love between two individuals. It is when a couple feels a connection and heartbeat that they cannot explain. It means spiritual closeness, selfless love (agape) with your partner, and accepting them wholly, flaws and all. Most importantly, it means having a God-centred relationship where God is the foundation of your relationship, helping it survive any trial, tribulation, or test of time," he continued, striking the audience's hearts with his words.

"Therefore, adopting a spiritual lifestyle is crucial for any relationship to grow. If your relationship with God is strong, everything else will fall into place. Pray with your partner, invite God to be the centre of your relationship, listen to your subconscious self, and open your heart to divine energy," he concluded.

The audience once again rose to their feet, applauding the wise words of Master Brown.

The one-week convention proved to be a success. James learned a great deal and made many self-discoveries regarding his role in strengthening his family relationships. He also made friends from different countries and faiths.

Upon returning to London with his family, James transformed entirely in his relationships. He felt the changes within himself and his relationships. Olivia and Emma began to enjoy spending extensive amounts of time with him. James observed positive changes and happiness in his life, grateful to God for realising the importance of family relationships.

Chapter Four

The ramification of Broken Relationships.

Start with an introduction to how broken relationships can affect not just you but the people around you. Broken relationships are the cause of broken families, for example, in the case of a divorced couple. Their children are affected by the split as well as the divorcees themselves.

What causes broken relationships? And the Consequences of a split.

Chapter Four

The Ramifications of Broken Relationships

> *Tears shed for broken relationships can only cease with the soothing balm of forgiveness; indeed, granting forgiveness to oneself and others is the most precious gift of all.*

The crisp air of a beautiful November morning in London danced through the open windows, inviting the sun's gentle rays to illuminate the cosy room. James couldn't hide his excitement as he emerged from meditation with Olivia and their little girl, Emma, quickly retreating to his bedroom. In recent times, James had developed an unbreakable bond with his family, filled with kindness and loving associations. As Olivia and Emma made their way to the kitchen to prepare breakfast,

James' heart was filled with anticipation for a long-awaited reunion with his college best friend, Brian.

With his favourite café from their college years, Rose Café, as the meeting place, James set out for his trip. Located within walking distance from Brixton Station, he couldn't help but smile with every step. As he joined his family at the breakfast table, the happiness on his face couldn't be ignored. Looking at James' face with uncertain eyes, Olivia handed him a fried toast. He could understand her gaze, smiling without a word. "You are blushing today. Is everything alright?" Olivia inquired.

"I am pleased today!" James replied with a spark in his eyes.

"Can I know the reason behind your utmost happiness?" she asked, pouring orange juice into a glass.

"Today, after six years, I am going to meet my college best friend, Brian," he revealed. Olivia had never seen such an intense radiance in James' eyes before.

She took a bite of her toast and said, "I have never seen such happiness and excitement on your face before. This is all over meeting someone. It is not the first time you are going to meet your college friend. There is something special, isn't it?"

Knowing his wife wouldn't rest until she discovered the reason for his joy, James chuckled before responding. "Olivia! Brian was a life-changer for me. I told you about him before. Until now, I consider him the reason behind my golden step into this perfect life journey. If he hadn't intervened and taken me to the lecture that day, I wouldn't be the person I am today. So, I am very fortunate that God made him the source of my change. Everyone has a source, and mine was Brian."

James began sharing with Olivia about his dear friend Brian, describing his remarkable personality, divine mindset, and exceptional qualities. As James spoke, Olivia was able to recall the profound impact Brian had on her husband's life and how he was always a topic of discussion whenever James reminisced about his university days. With deep affection, Olivia then bestowed a passionate kiss on James, wishing him all the best for his upcoming meeting with Brian.

As lunchtime approached, James made his way to Rose Café, eagerly anticipating Brian's arrival. Upon entering, the patrons and staff were taken aback by James' glowing demeanour, seated alone at a round table. Suddenly, an older man approached him and commented on how he had never seen someone sitting so contently alone before, except for one reason. James couldn't help but chuckle at the older man's comment. When he mentioned that he was waiting for his college best friend, the old man sceptically asked if it was a girl or boy, to which James answered with a resounding "A boy!" Despite the older man's doubtful look, James eagerly awaited Brian's arrival.

As Brian walked in, James could barely contain his excitement and shouted with joy, "Oh, look at him! He's coming!" The older man gave Brian a quick once-over, noting his tired and worn appearance with a nod. As he left the table, he patted James on the shoulder and bid them farewell. James hugged Brian with great enthusiasm, asking how he was doing. Brian replied that he was good, though his demeanour suggested otherwise. James couldn't help but notice the signs of exhaustion and asked if everything was alright again.

Brian replied, "I'm good," but James pressed on, sensing something was amiss.

Brian asked James to elaborate on his expectations as they sat down to their drinks, giving him a funny and probing look. James couldn't help but notice how tired Brian looked and asked again if everything was okay. Brian replied with a noncommittal "Hmm," and James remarked on how they seemed to have returned to their college days, with both of them now sharing similar demeanours — James looking energetic and fresh, while Brian appeared worn out and dull. They both laughed, acknowledging that time had passed, and they now led vastly different lives. Although much had changed, and they hadn't spoken in years, James was happy to catch up and answer Brian's questions.

James could discern a peculiar melancholy etched on Brian's face, which caught him off guard. He had envisioned a more vibrant and livelier demeanour from his old friend, especially after hearing about his recent return from Dubai and the fatherhood of two gorgeous children. His mind raced with questions, and he couldn't help but feel anxious to know why Brian had been out of touch and distant for so long.

"Brian, tell me what has happened these years, old chap. Why did you cut me off and not call? I have been yearning to catch up with you and have so much to ask!" James inquired, with genuine concern on his face as he glanced at Brian's visibly stressed expression.

"Let it go, dear," Brian said, taking a swig from his drink, trying to deflect the conversation.

"But what do you mean?" James pressed, placing his glass back on the table. "You are my brother from another mother. I need to know why you've been absent from my life."

"Drop it! Let's talk about your life and family," Brian attempted to steer the discussion away from himself.

James surveyed Brian's countenance closely, and he could tell that his friend was not in a good state, mentally or emotionally. It was evident that he needed support and care, and James was determined to provide it. "My life is splendid, and my family is a true gift," James replied, fixing his gaze on Brian's face, searching for answers. "How about yours?" he inquired, sensing underlying anger and immense sorrow brewing within Brian.

"Good," Brian replied with a wry smile that didn't match his words.

"Your words don't match your expression. What's going on, Brian?" James asked, concerned.

Brian remained silent, unable to answer James' probing questions. He tried to hide his troubles, as he had done with other friends, but James was different. James knew him too well and could decipher his emotions from his body language without any words exchanged. "I have to head back to the office after lunch. I started a new job here in London and can't risk getting fired in my second week. I don't have the time to discuss this right now," Brian said, looking at his watch.

"Alright, I understand. But we need to plan our next meet-up. When can we talk again?" James asked impatiently.

Brian remained silent, hesitant to confront the situation at hand. However, James was not one to let him off the hook easily. "You will come over to my house on Sunday. Is that settled?" James proposed.

"No, let's meet here again," Brian replied suddenly, seemingly willing to entertain the idea of a future discussion.

"Absolutely!" James beamed with the agreement; his heart filled with brotherly love. It wasn't until their meeting that day that he truly realized how much he had missed Brian. Tears glistened in Brian's eyes as he hastily departed, leaving James without a chance to speak or reach out to him.

As James returned home, his mind was consumed with thoughts of Brian. He couldn't shake the feeling that something was off with his brother. His unease remained palpable despite his efforts to maintain a positive demeanour during dinner. James didn't want to burden his family with his troubled emotions. After a refreshing shower, he settled into bed, where his loving wife Olivia asked about his day.

"Um…it was…normal and surprising," James murmured in response.

Olivia picked up on his subdued tone and prodded him for more information. James opened up to her, confessing his worries about Brian. He was convinced that something was amiss, that his brother was carrying a heavy burden that he couldn't share. Olivia listened attentively, offering her support and suggesting that James reach out to Brian again. "You should invite him to our home this time," Olivia suggested. "Maybe he'll be more comfortable opening up in a familiar environment." James was heartened by Olivia's encouragement and revealed that he had already extended an invitation to Brian, but his brother had requested they meet at the café again on Sunday.

As James prepared to meet Brian on Sunday, his mind raced with countless thoughts and concerns. He took a deep breath, attempting to dispel his anxious thoughts before arriving at the café. Despite his efforts, James couldn't shake the sense that something was wrong with Brian. When Brian finally arrived, James was struck by how tired and worn out he appeared. He was cold and distant, looking like someone who hadn't slept in weeks. James hoped he could help his brother ease his burden and find the peace he needed.

"Hello Brian, it's such a delight to see you," James rose from his seat, his voice exuding warmth and happiness. Brian replied in the same rough tone, but James could see the tiredness etched on his face. "Are you alright?" James inquired, concern evident in his voice as he studied Brian's expression.

"Yes, I'm fine. Don't tell me I look tired again," Brian replied, a hint of a smile on his lips.

"Of course not," James chuckled. "I have ordered some delectable delicacies to invigorate your droopy demeanour."

"Much obliged," Brian replied gratefully.

Rather than dwelling on Brian's present state of mind, James opted to delve into their fond memories, reliving the games and adventures of their past. They chatted and laughed over lamb suya, fried plantains, and Jollof rice, savouring the flavours and the joy of each other's company. After some time, James noticed a glimmer of happiness returning to Brian's face. "James," Brian spoke up, his voice slightly choked, "can you believe I laughed today after such a long time?"

James beamed at the sight of his friend's newfound contentment. "That smile looks priceless on your face, Brian," James leaned in and said, admiring his friend's glowing countenance.

Brian's eyes filled with tears as he smiled, touched by James' words. "Hey, Brian," James said, coming closer to his chair, "you know you can't hide anything from me, right?"

Brian turned to face him; his expression was pensive. "Yes, I know," he replied, his voice wavering slightly.

"Then tell me everything," James demanded gently, his concern palpable. "I want to know what's going on. You're getting me worried." Brian attempted to deflect the conversation, but James was not having it. "Brian, if you don't tell me what's wrong, you won't be leaving without me by your side," James warned, clenching his fist.

"I wish," Brian replied, his voice laden with longing.

James was taken aback by Brian's response, unsure what to make of it. He stood up and gestured for Brian to follow him. "Come with me," James said firmly.

Without resistance, Brian stood up, and the two of them walked out of the café, the cool evening breeze enveloping them. As they walked, they stopped to take in the breathtaking sunset, the colours painting the sky a magnificent hue. James finally broke the silence, his voice hesitant. "How have you changed so much, Brian? You used to be the one attending those inspiring lectures." The words hung in the air, and Brian's expression turned thoughtful, lost in his musings.

"After I graduated and went to Dubai, the intellectual discourse and teachings that once shaped my life were left behind. I was fortunate to secure a lucrative position in a company that rewarded me with a lavish house and car, making my parents, friends, and family proud. I savoured the good life as a single man, basking in the glory of my accomplishments.

"One fateful night, everything changed when I witnessed a terrible accident on my way home. Moved by an innate sense of compassion, I rushed to help the victims. Amidst the chaos, I noticed a young woman fighting for her life, covered in blood. I sprang into action, providing her with much-needed emotional and financial support. As we spent more time together, we grew fond of each other and eventually fell in love.

"My beloved Abijah, now my wife, was a gentle and kind-hearted soul whose pure nature was the object of my admiration. Even her friends were decent, courteous couples. Our relationship was harmonious; we tied the knot after six months, looking forward to a long and happy life together. However, my happiness was short-lived. After the birth of our daughter, Mia, Abijah underwent a drastic transformation, becoming rude and distant towards me. I struggled to comprehend why she would act this way despite providing her and our family with a luxurious lifestyle."

As the sun set, casting a golden glow across the sky, Brian shared his tale with James, who listened attentively, knowing that this was a rare moment of vulnerability. Brian took a deep breath, his fingers fumbling in his jacket pocket as he retrieved a pair of gloves. James followed suit, carefully adjusting his scarf before donning his gloves.

"I thought things were bad at that time," Brian continued. "I wanted to go back to our happier days before Mia was born. But after the arrival of our son, Jack, our relationship grew more strained. Now, Abijah lives with Jack at her parents' house while Mia stays with me. But with my demanding job, I can't give her the care she deserves. To make matters worse, my parents have taken Abijah's side, and they're not even speaking to me." Brian turned towards James and said, "Now, you must be thinking that I am a pitiful case."

"No, I don't think that way. It's not a challenging situation. Instead, I wish to shake some sense into you for worrying excessively about such a trivial problem," James said, playfully nudging Brian's elbow.

"Are you out of your mind?" Brian's ear flushed with embarrassment. "My wife decided to leave me, and you're saying it's not a big deal."

"Listen, do you want to leave her?" James inquired.

"James, I'm just worried about my children," Brian expressed with immense emotion.

"Alright. We'll manage," James said reassuringly. James observed Brian's vexed expression and added, "Don't fret. Come to my place with your family, and we'll find the best solution together."

"She won't agree," Brian replied curtly.

"Don't give up without trying," James retorted sternly.

"Okay," Brian acquiesced.

"You had me ruminating over all sorts of reasons for your unhappiness, not realising we can fix it," James said thoughtfully.

"It's too late," Brian replied dismally.

"As long as you're still breathing, it's never too late," James replied optimistically. Realizing how far they had walked, they mutually agreed to hail a black cab back to the café, where they'd parked their cars. They expressed gratitude to each other and looked forward to their next meeting.

Days passed swiftly, and on the following Sunday, Brian's family was at James' house. Olivia sat with Abijah in the living room while their children played in front of them. Emma was delighted with her two new friends, Mia and Jack. Mia and

Emma were the same age, and three-year-old Jack played with Emma's toys, rolling around on the mat. Olivia shared her story of love and marriage with Abijah. Then, after some time, James and Brian entered the room. On that day, Brian appeared relatively better, or perhaps he consciously tried to put on a cheerful demeanour.

With a bright smile, James looked at Emma and Mia playing together and exclaimed, "What's going on over there?"

Emma met her father's gaze and replied, "Daddy, I have a new friend."

James was overjoyed and patted her head, "That's wonderful news!" Brian also noticed the delight on Mia's face.

"I think they're enjoying each other's company," Abijah observed, watching the girls play.

"Yes, they are. And now, you have another reason to visit us more often," Olivia said with a warm smile. Abijah and Brian exchanged uncertain glances. "I mean, this is now your daughter's friend's house too. So, it would be great if you could visit more often," Olivia clarified.

Mia immediately chimed in with excitement, "Yes!" Everyone couldn't help but laugh at her spontaneous response. After dinner, Brian's family prepared to leave. Emma and Mia were feeling a bit down that they had to part, but Brian reassured her that they would come to visit again soon. After their conversation, both children were happy again…

As James was getting ready for bed that night, Olivia called him, "James, I don't have any negative feelings towards Abijah after tonight's gathering. She seems like a lovely person. I'm not sure why they're not happy together. They complement each other so well," Olivia shared.

James looked out the window and replied, "There is only one reason why most couples break up, which I've seen in almost all the cases we've dealt with at the Youth Club. It's the lack of emotional intimacy, usually caused by a lack of time and a communication breakdown. Do you remember Master Benaiah's lecture?"

"Yes, I do," Olivia confirmed.

"That's what they need in their relationship, and they need our help to guide them through that process," James declared.

The following week was full of activities for James. It was the Mega Week conference event at the Youth Club, which required a lot of preparation and management. While many other experts assisted him, James still had to do much of the work himself. Additionally, he and other Youth Club staff were also planning a Book Fair.

With a kind and empathetic tone, James reflected on the events during the Mega Week event. Instead of giving lectures, James had the pleasure of inviting world-famous scholars and his mentors to attend. Although James had invited Brian to the event, he could not attend due to work obligations. Despite this, the week was deemed successful by the Youth Club's staff.

After the event, James couldn't help but think about meeting Brian once again. He decided to take action and visited Brian's office the following day. Upon seeing James, Brian stood up from his chair with warmth and politeness.

Apologizing for not being able to connect with Brian during the Mega Week event, James shared how much his family enjoyed spending time with Brian's family. Brian responded positively and shared that Mia loved it as well.

However, the conversation suddenly turned when James asked Brian about his relationship with Abijah. Brian's response was unexpected, saying that he believed divorce was the only solution to their problems. James was taken aback and asked for further details on the matter.

Brian explained that during their ride home after the gathering at James' house, he had expressed his desire to work on their relationship for the sake of their children. However, Abijah erupted in anger and took Mia with her. Brian believed that he had done nothing wrong and only wanted his family back for the sake of their children's upbringing.

James listened patiently and asked a series of questions to get to the root of the issue. He suggested that Brian's choice of words may have hurt Abijah's feelings and self-esteem, leading to her outburst. James emphasised the importance of carefully choosing words before speaking, especially towards close loved ones like a spouse.

James approached the conversation with a kind and compassionate demeanour, seeking to understand the issues and provide helpful insights to his friend.

"How frigid are your words! In marriage, words like 'we,' 'us,' and 'ours' are supposed to be used, yet I can't help but notice you consistently use 'I' or 'my kids,' hardly ever saying 'our children.' The reality is if you learned to substitute 'me,' 'I,' and 'mine' in your relationships, things might transform. Did you know that people end up in dire situations, even in prison or worse, just because of the words they use? And your body language accounts for approximately 70% of your communication skills. Frankly, my friend, your body language doesn't do you any favours. Therefore, before salvaging your relationship, you must first relinquish your ego and anger," James advised with a gentle tone.

"Okay, James, are you suggesting that I shouldn't use those words in a taunting manner towards her? But hold on a second, you can't judge me based on one conversation," Brian was starting to become irate. "If you delve deep into all our issues, you'll realise she's at fault."

"Okay," James attempted to ease his tension. "Are you implying that you've been playing fair since the beginning of your relationship with Abijah? Let's get to the root of the problem," he said while observing Brian's stressed expression.

"What are some things you dislike about Abijah?" he added.

"I don't like it when she argues with me. She nit-picks everything I do and says, sometimes making me feel unwelcome in my own home. I just want to live in peace, but she seems to thrive on conflict, and it's eroding our relationship. She starts arguing over the smallest things. For instance, if I unintentionally misplace a towel, she begins to nag. I don't have any problems with her," Brian explained, looking at James. "But the thing is, she makes me feel insignificant in front of her. I took this job and worked tirelessly for her and our children's future. However, I don't recall her ever expressing gratitude for my efforts. I work this hard solely to provide a comfortable lifestyle for her and our children. A simple thank you or acknowledgement would suffice."

"Brian," James leaned in. "you're saying that your partner doesn't value you in your marriage, causing you to feel worthless. However, my question is: Do you value her or acknowledge her contributions?"

"I am constantly occupied with work, striving to be a dedicated provider. The fruit of my labour is a decent income, but I wonder for whom I am doing it?" Brian confided in James.

James responded, "Brian, your wife doesn't need you to exhaust yourself with work constantly. Do you remember how much time you spent together before these clashes? How much time do you spend with her now?"

Brian remained silent, pondering James' words.

"You want your wife to value you, yet you are not showing her the same appreciation. Spending quality time with your partner is one way of showing that they matter to you," James continued.

Interrupting James, Brian exclaimed, "Listen, James! I don't want any more relationship advice. I don't want to dampen my mood further. Divorce is my final decision, and I ask that you not discuss our relationship anymore, for God's sake!"

Anxiety, a lack of self-control, and anger were evident on Brian's face. James knew that Brian was struggling in his relationship and that talking about saving it at this point was useless.

"Alright," James replied softly, hoping to make Brian realize his loud and abrupt tone. Brian felt ashamed after hearing James' gentle response.

"I am sorry, James. My mind is not functioning well at present," Brian confessed, holding onto his hair. "What I am going through is eating me up inside. I am extremely sorry for my behaviour."

James smiled at Brian's apology and patted his back. "Don't worry, bro! I understand that you are mentally distressed about this issue in your life." He poured a glass of water and handed it to Brian.

After a few seconds of silence, James asked, "So, you believe that granting her a divorce will improve your life?"

"Yes, I hope so!" replied Brian.

"And what about your children? Who will they live with?" James inquired gently.

"I wish I could keep them with me, but unfortunately, I can't," Brian replied with a pained expression and teary eyes.

James asked politely, "Why can't you keep them?"

Silence fell heavily in the room, broken only by the steady gaze of James as he looked into Brian's eyes. Brian's heart felt like it had been sliced into pieces with a sharp blade as he struggled with the question spinning in his mind: "Why are my children not attached to me?"

James gently interjected, asking Brian to consider the lifestyle his children deserved, given his decision to divorce and leave them. He wondered aloud whether Brian was confident they would truly get what they deserved under these circumstances. Brian's voice broke as he explained that he had provided his family with a great life and how hard it was for a single parent to maintain such a lifestyle.

James poured water into a glass with his characteristic calmness and posed a poignant question: "How do you want your children to react when they see you in the future?" He wondered whether they would embrace him with gratitude for a wonderful childhood or would they be disgusted and resentful for being left alone when they needed him the most.

As Brian grappled with the weight of these thoughts, James set his glass down and spoke softly, "I think it is the best decision you have ever made. I am sorry I couldn't understand it at first." James then turned his attention to the files on the table, detailing the benefits of Brian's new job. He highlighted the peace it would offer, the substantial income he could earn, and the freedom to work all day and night without distractions.

Brian couldn't shake the feeling that James' words had pierced his heart and soul. Just then, James remembered meeting the daughter of another divorced friend, Mr Sesay. James asked her if she missed her father, and her response took him aback: 'No. My father is a loser and a deadbeat. I wish he was dead!' James was speechless, wondering if the young girl's words were hers or something she had heard from her mother.

In a matter of moments, the sound of James' phone rang out, displaying the name "Wife" on the screen. A wide smile stretched across his face as he glanced at his phone. "Please excuse me for a moment," James said, turning to Brian with an apologetic look. As he answered the phone, his demeanour changed instantly. Joy and love radiated from his face as he spoke to his Emma.

Brian couldn't help but notice the remarkable transformation in James' countenance. *Why are my children not attached to me?* Brian's thoughts continued to trouble him. He wondered if it was because he had failed to spend enough quality time with them. Attempting to recall his conversations with his children, particularly his daughter, Mia, Brian drew a blank.

"Okay, Emma, Daddy will talk to you later. Love you, my little princess," James concluded his conversation with his daughter, placing the phone back on the table. "So, where were we?" James asked nonchalantly. Brian remained silent, his face a jumble of conflicting emotions. James noticed his friend's unease and attempted to lighten the mood. "Hey, buddy! You've decided to divorce Abijah and leave your children to pursue your happiness. So why the long face? We should be celebrating!"

James exclaimed, a twinkle in his eye. But Brian couldn't shake off the words that had penetrated his heart.

"Okay, I must go now. Emma is waiting for me, as I've promised to take her to the park," James chuckled and stood up from his seat, his face radiating with fatherly love and joy. "Bye," he said with a warm smile and left the room, leaving behind a sense of positivity and hope; after putting Brian on an introspective journey of evaluating his role as a father and husband, James left.

Brian had turned off all the lights in the room, feeling overwhelmed and lost in thought. It was as if a veil had been lifted from his eyes, and he could finally see the true nature of his relationship with his family. He realised he had quickly blamed Abijah for their problems without considering his actions and shortcomings. His heart was heavy with regret in the dark room, and tears streamed down his face. He cried like a baby, releasing all the pent-up emotions he had suppressed for so long.

Meanwhile, James had returned home, feeling a sense of melancholy and doubt. He couldn't shake off the image of Brian's distraught face from his mind. He wondered if he had pushed him too far, but deep down, he knew it was necessary for Brian's growth and self-awareness. As he sat on the couch, Olivia noticed his solemn demeanour and asked him with concern, "Is everything okay, my love?"

Taking a deep breath, James replied, "Brian had decided to leave," his voice filled with sadness and regret. "I hope I didn't hurt him too much with my words." Olivia listened quietly, her heart heavy with concern for James and Brian. Though she wanted to ask more questions, she respected James' feelings and let him be.

After enjoying a delicious dinner, James retreated to his room to unwind. He refreshed himself with a soothing shower before sitting at his study desk. With his trusty black pen in hand, he began jotting down his thoughts in his diary.

'After over four years, I finally reunited with my college best friend, Brian. I expected him to be a wise sage and a spiritual guru because he used to attend lectures on various topics in our small auditorium. However, upon meeting him, I realized that he had transformed into a completely different person, one who was grappling with a strained relationship with his family. I tried my best to help him see things clearly, but he remained oblivious to the issues at hand. After observing the couple closely, I understood that they lacked emotional intimacy, communication, and quality family time.'

James paused to contemplate and then continued writing, 'As I reflect on this situation, I can't help but remember my college years. I had contemplated suicide because I was headed in the wrong direction. My parents' lack of understanding about my life and their emphasis on grades caused immense pressure. Even now, it feels like I am living a similar rat race life. At the time, I believed my parents were heartless and wrong and that the world was against me. I felt misunderstood and unloved.'

James stopped again, overcome with emotion. 'As a result, I developed addictions and unhealthy habits. I became anaemic and lost my appetite due to severe depression and a damaged relationship with my friends and family. Bitterness and distrust clouded my behaviour, and I wanted to isolate myself from the tragic world. All these things I now see in Brian. It's painful to witness him in the same hurtful condition.'

His heart heavy with sorrow, James continued writing, 'It's clear that the lack of quality family time can lead to bigger issues. I experienced the same thing when I was struggling with trust and understanding, ultimately leading to extreme stress and depression. And now, Brian is going through similar troubles in his relationship due to the lack of importance. Realizing that partners' diminished importance in each other's hearts directly results from the lack of shared moments and intimacy is alarming. Nowadays, most families have little to no time for each other.'

James glanced up and composed his final thoughts as the beautiful wall clock chimed midnight.

'I yearn to find a way to salvage his relationship, for single parenting may lead to mental distress for children and spark turmoil in their life's journey. It can also place an enormous burden on one parent, leading to bitterness within the family unit.

'While some single parents excel at raising children and their offspring have gone on to become prominent figures in society, it is paramount and significant for children to be raised by both parents living together under one roof, in harmony, if feasible.'

As James closed his diary, his thoughts still lingered on Brian as he searched for a way to reconcile their bond. The morning brought about his usual routine of overseeing the final touches of the Youth Club's building with Emma by his side. The contractors were doing a remarkable job, and things were going smoothly. He then took Emma for a walk in the park, where the dew-covered grass was neatly trimmed. They sat down on the lush green grass, basking in the refreshing aura of the universe while meditating.

Despite the cold morning, the refreshing air lifted James' spirits as Emma got up and began to play around him. As James watched her, she ran through the park with her hair fluttering in the wind, wearing a priceless smile on her face.

As he kept a watchful eye on her, she dashed towards him, and he revelled in every moment of watching her play in the garden. *If only Brian could understand the value of family*, he thought to himself.

On the other side of town, Brian laid in bed, unable to sleep throughout the night, his eyes bloodshot. He spent the entire time reflecting on his family, analysing his relationships, and acknowledging his faults, searching for a resolution to his troubles. However, his mind could not function properly due to immense pressure and stress. He knew that there was one person in the universe who could offer a solution.

He rose from his bed and picked up his mobile phone. "Hello, James!" he exclaimed upon dialling the number.

James was overjoyed and surprised on the other end of the line. "I would love to meet you today, if possible," Brian requested.

"Absolutely! See you in an hour," James replied before hanging up.

Brian then headed to the bathroom for a shower, dressed, and went to the local garden. While waiting for James, he paced back and forth, filled with nerves. Eventually, he discovered a comfortable spot beside a tree to sit and wait.

As James arrived, Brian leapt up from the bench and waved.

James greeted Brian with a warm smile, but his heart ached as he saw his friend's red, tired eyes and the slump in his shoulders. James could sense the weight of the world on Brian's shoulders.

"How are you, my friend?" James asked, his voice filled with concern and compassion.

As he listened to Brian's quiet reply, James couldn't help but notice the sadness etched on his face.

"I sense that something is troubling you, my friend," James said, placing a comforting hand on Brian's shoulder.

Brian sighed deeply, his eyes searching James for answers. "James, I am lost. I fear that I am failing as a father and husband, and it's tearing me apart."

James nodded in understanding, "I can see that you are hurting, Brian. But don't worry, my friend. We will find a way to fix this." James listened with empathy and understanding as Brian opened up about his struggles. He could see that Brian had reached a turning point in his life, and he was ready to make changes.

"Brian, it may seem difficult, but remember that nothing worth having comes easy. If you truly want to save your family and protect your children's future, then you must put in the work. Start by focusing on rebuilding your communication with Abijah and being more present in your family's life. This will take time, but I believe you can do it," James said, offering encouragement.

After a few moments of contemplative silence, Brian spoke with newfound clarity. "You're right, James. I've been so focused on my needs and desires that I failed to see the bigger picture. I need to take responsibility for my actions and work towards rebuilding my relationship with Abijah. I want to be the father and husband that my family deserves."

James smiled, relieved that his friend was willing to make changes. "I believe in you, Brian. You can do this. Take it one step at a time, and always keep your family's best interests at heart."

Brian's countenance was overcome with a heavy shame as he confessed to his best friend about having infidelity. He spoke from the depths of his soul, trying to justify his actions while bearing the weight of his guilt.

As his friend listened in shock, he couldn't help but express his concern. He reminded Brian of the severity of the situation and the fact that he had broken a sacred vow in his marriage. The devil had taken centre stage in their relationship, and he had allowed someone else to intrude into his sacred union.

Despite the gravity of the situation, James maintained a compassionate tone as he addressed his friend. He acknowledged that society often treated infidelity as a norm but questioned whether it was acceptable behaviour. He argued that true love requires going above and beyond for the ones we cherish, not causing them unbearable pain.

Brian interrupted, tears streaming down his face, and expressed his love for his family. He felt lonely and unfulfilled in his marriage, leading him to make a deeply regretted mistake.

James shared his insights, reflecting on how work and other distractions can cause people to neglect their families. He stressed the importance of balance and attention within a family unit. He reminded Brian that making things right only takes self-realization and acceptance.

As James discussed the importance of communication and quality time in a relationship, Brian felt hopeless. He felt that it was too late and that he had already caused irreparable damage.

But James refused to let his friend fall into despair. He encouraged Brian to remain positive and start incorporating affirmations into his life. He assured him it wasn't too late to save his relationship and his family's future. Communication and quality time were the keys to fixing the damage that had been done.

"Brian, my dear friend," James began with a soft, gentle tone, "do you remember when you used to describe your relationship with Abijah as brilliant as if the stars in the sky were brighter because of your love? You two were inseparable, like two peas in a pod, and your bond was unbreakable. You knew each other inside out, and your love was so strong that you believed you were soulmates destined to be together forever. But now, things have changed."

James paused to sip his water, letting the silence linger before continuing, "After marriage, life happened, and you got caught up in your work. You started prioritising other things over your marriage, and the distance between you and Abijah grew before you knew it. Your communication became less frequent, and when you did talk, it was often filled with arguments and defensive behaviour. It's not your fault, my friend, but it is something you need to address."

He looked at Brian with a knowing expression, "I'm sure you love your wife, but when was the last time you expressed it to her? When did you last take her out on a romantic date or just sit down and listen to her feelings? Small gestures can go a long way in keeping a relationship strong. It's crucial to have regular relationship reviews where you both express your needs and wants without fear of hurting each other."

James saw the tears welling up in Brian's eyes but continued, "I'm not here to blame you or Abijah for the state of your relationship. It takes two people to tango, as they say. But it only takes one person to start making changes and reignite the spark in a relationship. It's up to you, my friend, to take the reins and steer your relationship back on track. Don't let your ego or pride get in the way of saving your marriage."

He leaned closer to Brian, "God has given you a chance to save your marriage and family. It's a precious gift that not everyone gets, so don't waste it. Work on your relationship because sometimes, what seems shiny and perfect from afar is nothing but an illusion. Remember, my friend, not all that glitters is gold."

As James listened to his brother's words, tears of relief and happiness flowed down his cheeks. He was overwhelmed with emotion as James hugged him tightly and reassured him that everything would be okay. The warmth of his brother's embrace comforted him, and he knew he was lucky to have such a caring sibling.

When he returned home, James rushed towards Olivia and embraced her tightly. He wept with a mixture of grief and joy, overwhelmed by the emotions he had kept bottled up for so long. Although he had tried to be strong in front of Brian, he couldn't contain his feelings any longer.

Looking at his wife, he realized how lucky he was to have her by his side. He felt grateful for the opportunity to learn from Brian's situation and make amends in his marriage. He thanked God for the gift of family and the chance to heal relationships that had been broken.

Later that evening, Brian mustered the courage to visit his parents' house and speak with Abijah. He arrived dressed in a handsome blue three-piece suit, looking both confident and vulnerable at the same time. When Abijah answered the door, she was surprised to see him but was struck by his innocent glow and the sincerity in his voice.

As they sat in the Rose Café, Abijah couldn't understand why Brian was so attentive and affectionate. She felt like she was in a dream when he apologized to her for everything, he had put her and their children through. His voice was full of deep pain and sorrow, and his eyes were teary as he asked for her forgiveness.

Brian held her hands tightly, promising he would never hurt her again. Abijah felt moved by his words and was willing to give him one last chance. She knew that forgiveness was not easy, but she also knew true love was worth fighting for.

His words were like music to her soul, leaving her speechless. Tears welled up in her eyes as she gazed at Brian's face, unable to express her feelings. Her silence and tears were like daggers to Brian's heart, making him painfully aware of his mistakes. Eventually, the tears began to roll down her cheeks, and Brian couldn't bear to see her cry. "I'm sorry, I'm so sorry!" he cried, rising from his chair and rushing towards her. She wept bitterly as she rested her head on his broad chest, and they both wept silently, lost in their emotions.

Headed home, Brian was constantly beaming with joy, and Abijah couldn't help but ask him what had brought this sudden change. "What's gotten into you?" she queried.

Brian turned to her with a smirk on his face, "I realized my life is dull without our spats," he quipped. Abijah had expected him to say something romantic, but she couldn't help but chuckle at his comment.

Upon arriving at Brian's parent's home, he instructed Abijah to quickly gather their children without wasting time packing anything. "Come back with Mia and Jack right away. You know I can't enter that house with our current situation," he explained as he opened the car door for her. Abijah was happy to see him taking the initiative to mend their relationship, and she hoped to reconcile with him. She knew divorce would only harm their children, and she couldn't bear raising them as a single parent.

With Brian's positive actions, their marriage took a different turn, and they began to feel like newlyweds. Brian hugged and kissed his children, and Abijah couldn't help but smile as she watched them. James was right when he said that a relationship doesn't break because of one person, and Brian realized this. His good behaviour had melted Abijah's heart, and she, too, was determined to make a significant step in their marriage.

When James invited them to his house, they all shared laughter and jokes, reminiscing about their college days. Emma and Mia had made their circle, playing and laughing as their parents chatted. Mia's innocent words about how much she loved seeing her parents laugh brought tears to Brian's eyes. He realized how much he had missed his family's laughter and joy and was grateful for this second chance.

At the dinner table, Brian was quiet, lost in thought. James noticed his silence and asked what was on his mind. Brian turned to Abijah with a warm, friendly smile and said, "Abijah, you asked me about my change? The main reason behind it is James' words." Abijah looked at James with admiration, but James didn't want to take the credit. However, Brian hushed him with a finger on his lips before he could say anything. "No, James, you were right," he said, his eyes shining with gratitude. They all smiled, happy to be together again, knowing their love was stronger than ever before.

"So, James is the person that made me realize the unparalleled importance of a family life," he said, turning towards Abijah. "He gave me an entirely different and illuminating angle to see my role in our relationship. His presence in my life is simply a divine blessing. He made me introspect and reflect upon myself. His words and motivation were like a pair of crystal-clear eyeglasses for me at that moment, and it made me perceive our relationship for the first time in a more profound and loving dimension." Brian hadn't stopped gazing at James and Abijah side by side as if savouring a moment frozen in time. "I want to thank you, James, from the bottom of my heart, for making me recognize my mistake and saving my life from going awry. You've shown me what true friendship is. You're not just my friend anymore, James; you're my dearest brother for life," Brian said, beaming with gratitude as he turned to James. Then he leaned closer towards Abijah and said, "And I also want to thank you, my dear Abijah, for forgiving me and accepting me once again."

Everyone at the table could see the priceless smile on Abijah's face, illuminating the room with her radiant happiness. Although she hadn't spoken a word, her moist eyes spoke volumes, expressing her inner contentment and joy. "Alright, alright! The sumptuous food is getting cold," Olivia said smilingly.

"Let's hurry up and start eating folks!" James exclaimed, flourishing the bowl of fragrant rice near his side. Abijah and Brian smiled and started savouring the delicious dinner, their taste buds tingling with delight. James and Olivia could also feel exceptional contentment in their hearts, observing them sitting and eating together joyfully, savouring the moments of happiness and love life had to offer. "Having a friend is good, but choosing the right friendship is a rare and wondrous blessing," Abijah whispered tenderly in Brian's ear, filling his heart with warmth and love.

Chapter Five

Conflict and Forgiveness – To Stay or Walk Away?

It discusses the coming together of two different minds and what it means for the couple and loved ones, Things that cause conflict in intimate relationships, How to deal with conflicts, and What if my spouse refuses to resolve conflict when it is time to stay or walk away from a relationship.

Chapter Five

Conflict and Forgiveness – To Stay or Walk Away?

When two brilliant minds collaborate, the outcome can be flawless.

*J*ames was graced with a dream of the Youth Club. In his vision, he strolled towards the Youth Club and saw a divine light radiating from the heavens. Angels were etching words of wisdom onto the walls of the club. As James awakened, he recollected every phrase scripted on the walls. Then, he had to impart a lecture based on those words and implement them onto the walls of the Youth Club.

The Youth Club's architecture was resplendent, illuminating the entire vicinity with grandeur lights hanging effortlessly from every side of the structure. The azure tint with rainbow stripes running across one side of the wall was emitting inspirational messages from the top projector. A colossal box was situated on the right-hand side of the entrance, inviting individuals to share their requests, suggestions, prayers, critiques, expressions of gratitude, and much more. One of the windows was embellished with a stained-glass design, casting an array of hues into the building.

Vibrant light colours swirled around the stage, and a table was positioned in front of it, adorned with a grand Bible and the Quran. The entire layout was intricately crafted, exuding a warm and inviting ambience suitable for individuals of all ages and backgrounds. One of the sanctums within the club was christened 'Lights of Hope.' Inside this chamber, a circular block filled with sand awaited the arrival of visitors who desired to light candles and offer prayers for their cherished ones. The walls were adorned with diverse inscriptions of petitions, while the English versions of the holy Quran and Bible were conveniently available for all to peruse. 'God Answers Prayers' was inscribed boldly on one of the walls, serving as a constant reminder of divine benevolence.

Another chamber, however, was relatively austere, containing nothing but a plush carpet and a magnificent painting of the ocean and sunrise. A renowned artist had generously donated the painting to the Youth Club, adorning one of the walls. A few phrases adorned another wall, inspiring visitors: 'You Are What You Think,' 'Positivity is in the Mindset,' and 'Use Your Creativity Wisely.' This room was accessible to all, 24/7, every day of the year, and was situated separately from the main hall, accessible only via a door with a unique code.

The main hall was resplendent every Saturday night, filled with individuals holding pens, paper, and an assortment of electronic devices. Everyone appeared captivated, intently listening to the speaker who stood tall on the elevated stage. With eloquent words, the speaker held the audience in a trance. The Youth Club's main hall was blessed with a gentle breeze that flowed through the large open windows, infusing the room with a soothing and calming atmosphere. The ideal temperature provided the perfect environment for the congregation to focus on the speaker's words. It was as though God's divine presence permeated the air, saturating the room with a sense of peace and tranquillity.

James addressed the audience, determined not to evade or dismiss the topic at hand. He spoke passionately, reminding everyone of the magnificence of planet Earth, the bounty of nature and its beauty, and how it was all intended for humans to cherish and appreciate. As he spoke, he gazed intently at the congregation, a look of deep contemplation in his eyes.

"Our relationships with our family, friends, parents, spouse, children, teachers, bosses, and all other living beings are a divine gift from the nurturing master of the universe," James declared with conviction.

"God wants us to cherish these relationships and live in harmony and love with one another. They bring us a sense of companionship and belonging and are the most significant blessing in our lives. In God's eyes, the most crucial relationship is that of a husband and wife."

As James paused to observe the congregation, he noticed they were avidly scribbling notes on their notepads and electronic devices, eager to capture every word he spoke. He gazed upon the audience, looking at him with awe and admiration. "Many of you are in relationships but uncertain about where they're headed.

"It's a common question to ask oneself, 'How do I know if this is the right person for me?' I know many of you desire healthy relationships. That's why it's essential to talk about marriage relationships in today's world. In my previous lectures, I discussed the betterment of premarital relationships between a man and a woman. But today, I want to focus on post-marital relationships, the relationship between a husband and wife," he said soothingly.

The calm wind breezed through the main hall. "I have strong reasons for wanting to discuss this topic in greater detail. First, if you assess your life, you'll realise that a significant portion revolves around post-marital relationships. Secondly, the increasing divorce rates are evident. It's crucial to talk about these relationships and nullify the myths that society has pushed into your minds," he continued.

Looking at the left-side wall clock, James smiled at the listeners. "Let's delve deeper into the combination of two minds. Honestly, every time I think about the concept of two human beings coming together, I'm mesmerised. This combination can occur through marriage or a bond of love. It's essential to remember that every human being on this planet is God's wonderful creature, whether they believe it or not. From the way of thinking, opinions about life and the universe, personality, character, nature, and even fingerprints, everything is unique."

"Each and every individual is unique, with their own perspective and way of viewing the world. Each person has their own living and loving standards, their own ideas of happiness, success, and even life and death. Every individual possesses an IQ and the gift of free will," James continued, his voice filled with wonder and admiration.

James paused to take a refreshing sip of water as he spoke, savouring the coolness as it flowed down his throat. "When two individuals with their own distinct personalities and characteristics come together, it is truly remarkable to see how they can become one unit. The power of the bond between them is simply incredible, whether it be through marriage or love. This power can transform two people by allowing them to indulge in each other's habits and characteristics and help solve mysterious problems they may face together."

James' face lit up with a beautiful smile, radiating joy and positivity to everyone in the room. "This power allows individuals with different ideologies to work together to solve life's challenges, to grow together and become better versions of themselves. It brings ease and comfort to those who possess completely different narratives. Truly, it is the power of love and the power of marriage that can unite and transform two unique individuals into one amazing unit."

As James spoke, he touched the hearts of his listeners and inspired them to have an open mindset about marriage. The audience was captivated, lost in the moment, without a care for time or place. James observed the audience with awe as he began to speak of soulmates, a concept that filled the room with a sense of wonder.

"Love," he explained, "is a force that brings two people together to create a bond unlike any other. This bond is so powerful that it can create soulmates, two individuals who are meant to be together in a way that transcends time and space."

James noted that there are two types of soulmates: those that God has brought together and those that individuals have brought together for their own reasons. To truly experience the magic of a soulmate, James emphasised the importance of ensuring that the person you choose to spend the rest of your life with is whom God has chosen for you. He cautioned that having great chemistry with someone does not necessarily mean they are your soulmate.

James shared that before he married Olivia, they fasted and prayed to make God the centre of their relationship, despite their powerful bond. He reminded the audience that many people get divorced because they were never truly soulmates to begin with. As James continued speaking, the audience was living and loving standards, how the power of love and marriage can transform two individuals into one united force. The words "I" and "You" no longer have a place in their vocabulary, replaced instead with the all-encompassing "We." Sadly, many people today misunderstand or misinterpret the power of this bond, especially during marriage.

When two individuals become soulmates, their opinions and thoughts merge into one, creating a beautiful harmony that is unparalleled in the universe. James explained that this bond is not only the most powerful but also the most beautiful in existence, as long as it is formed for the right reasons and with one's soulmate. He declared that this bond brings one closer to the divine, a connection that is beyond words.

James left the audience with a question, "How does this bond further bring us closer to our Lord?" and allowed them to contemplate the answer. "I am emphasising the powerful bond of love that results in marriage because it brings us closer to the divine. It is a gift from the Almighty, and all religious books emphasise its importance.

"It is a beautiful experience to observe your partner and be grateful for the magnificent human being they are. Just as parents thank God for their children, we must thank God for our partners. Looking at the history of the prophets, we can see that they also placed great importance on marriage because it is a divine order.

"Through marriage, we learn the lesson of acceptance and forgiveness, and we must use these lessons in our personal relationships. God wants us to love others just as He loves us." James checked the time on the wall clock and noticed that it was already 10:30 PM. He regretfully concluded the lecture for the night but promised to resume tomorrow from where he left off.

The audience stood up, applauding, as James made his way down from the stage to meet with Olivia and Emma. Many people came up to him to have a conversation, and he welcomed each one with warmth and kindness. Upon arriving home, Olivia headed straight to the kitchen to prepare dinner while Emma began to feel sleepy. James picked her up and placed her on his shoulders, giving her a gentle kiss on her head. Her beautiful hazel eyes opened, and she smiled brightly. "Daddy!" Emma exclaimed.

James responded softly, "Yes?"

"You're my superhero!" He couldn't help but chuckle at her sweet compliment.

Later, James sat down at the dinner table with Olivia while Emma had gone to bed. During their meal, Olivia asked, "Did you talk to Brian?"

"Yeah, I did. But I was at the Youth Club, so I couldn't talk to him in detail," James replied. Olivia simply nodded as she chewed her food. James remained optimistic and added, "I believe everything will be fine on his side."

Before retiring to bed, James went to his workspace, where he had a collection of books and a half-written paper on his study table. He looked out the window for a few moments before picking up three books: *Raising Good Humans, The Seven Principles for Making Marriage Work,* and *The Lost Art of*

Listening, and placing them on the side. He then proceeded to organise the rest of the books on his table.

The following morning, James was showering while Emma admired the beautiful morning scenery outside. She enjoyed the gentle caress of the cool breeze on her cheeks while the small birds chirped happily in the nest on the tree in front of their house. Olivia was preparing breakfast quickly, as she had to go to the restaurant afterwards. When they all sat down to eat in the kitchen, James enjoyed his toast and a freshly brewed cup of English tea with milk and no sugar. Suddenly, he closed his eyes and exclaimed, "Oh, my God!" Olivia and Emma looked at him curiously, wondering what was happening.

Olivia approached James with concern in her eyes as she asked, "Is everything okay with the toast, my love?"

James opened his eyes and instantly replied, "It's absolutely delicious!"

Olivia couldn't help but smile at his teasing, playfully biting her lip. "Why must you always tease me like this, James?" she asked, pretending to be annoyed. Their playful banter caused both father and daughter to share a laugh.

James took his wife's hand and looked into her eyes, "I just want you to know, my dear wife, that you are an amazing chef." The happiness on Olivia's face was unmistakable, a radiant glow that shone from within. This small family savoured their breakfast together, relishing in the simple joys of spending quality time with one another. Despite their busy schedules, they had grown closer through mutual respect and support for each other's responsibilities. After their lovely meal, Emma and Olivia left for school and the restaurant, respectively.

James made his way to the Youth Club, the warm atmosphere and friendly faces welcoming him as usual. As he walked through the main hall, his students eagerly greeted him, exclaiming, "Good morning, coach!" He beamed at the sight of their happiness and contentment, proud of his work and the connections he forged with these young minds. "We loved your lecture from yesterday!" one of the students said, a compliment that filled James' heart with pride and joy.

The doors of the Youth Club welcomed everyone with open arms, a place where students could gather and freely discuss various topics, ranging from life experiences to educational pursuits. "That's great!" James replied with a warm smile.

One of the students spoke up, "Sir, I first attended your lecture almost a year ago when you shared your life journey. Your story resonated with me because it felt like you were narrating my own story during my early college years. After that lecture, I joined the Youth Club, and my life changed completely."

James hugged him with genuine happiness and said, "Well done! I'm excited to share the rest of the lecture with you all."

As the students left to continue their day, James took a moment to reflect on his impact on other people's lives. He was grateful to God for allowing him to make a difference and cherished the countless stories of people whose lives he had touched. His greatest accomplishment was reuniting Brian with his wife, a moment, he will never forget. James thought *I should talk to him*, feeling the urge to check in on his friend. He found a bench in the Youth Club's Park and dialled Brian's number, but it was busy. So, he placed his phone on the bench beside him and took in the beauty of the morning.

Emma, his daughter, had inherited his love for nature, and James found himself smiling as he watched the small birds playing and fighting. Suddenly, his phone rang, and Brian's name appeared on the screen. James answered the phone, still smiling, and greeted his friend, "Hello, good morning, my dear friend!"

Brian's voice conveyed an infectious excitement and thrill as he greeted his friend, James. "Hey, my brother!" he replied with equal enthusiasm.

James quickly inquired about his friend's well-being, to which Brian replied that he was doing well. "I am fit and happy!" James responded softly. Brian noted that there was never a reason for James to be unhappy, as he was the most motivated and joyful person he had ever met. This prompted a hearty laugh from James. James then asked about the situation on Brian's end, to which Brian responded with some hesitation.

Although he said he was doing okay to some extent, James could detect a hint of sadness in his voice. When James pressed him further, Brian admitted that there was still work to be done to restore their relationship to their former state. James empathized with his friend and praised him for his patience and understanding. He lauded the principle that all things take time to heal, whether it be a bent iron or a damaged relationship. However, when Brian fell silent for a moment, James grew worried and called out to him. "Brian? Are you there?" he asked with concern. Brian assured him that he was still on the line and said everything was okay, but James could tell from his low voice that something was still bothering him. James rose from the bench, looking concerned.

"No, please tell me what's going on. I won't forgive myself if I don't help you," he said gently to Brian, who seemed to be hiding something.

Brian let out a small sigh. "I appreciate your concern, my friend. But I assure you that everything is fine. It just takes time for things to get back to normal," he reassured James.

"Is there anything I can do to support you?" James persisted.

Brian smiled at his friend's caring nature. "Thank you for your offer, James. Your friendship alone is enough to help me through this," he replied sincerely.

Suddenly, James had an idea. "Hey, why don't you come to my lecture tonight? It might lift your spirits," he suggested.

Brian hesitated for a moment before declining, "I would love to, but I already promised my family that we would go out for dinner tonight. But please let me know when your next lecture is. I'll make sure to attend," he said. James agreed and ended the call.

Later that night, the Youth Club was buzzing with activity as people eagerly awaited James' lecture. To them, it was more than just a speech; it was a spiritual experience that taught them how to live. The walls of the room glowed with different colours of lights, and the audience sat with pens and paper in hand, ready to absorb James' wisdom.

In a matter of moments, their beloved coach, Mr James, stepped onto the stage. The entire audience rose to their feet in warm welcome, showering him with affection and admiration. With his pure and gentle soul, melodious voice, and captivating way of speaking, James was an exceptional storyteller that captivated his listeners effortlessly. But something seemed off today. Despite the smile on his face, James appeared to be carrying a weight on his shoulders that was causing him to look a bit serious. He took a deep breath, trying to compose himself and focus on the lecture he was about to give.

"Welcome, everyone!" he began, projecting his voice to the audience. The cheers and applause that followed were tremendous, yet James was still visibly disturbed. He wanted to give his lecture with a clear mind, but something was bothering him. "Yesterday, we talked about the incredible power of two minds working together," James continued, gazing at the audience before him. "But today, I must apologize for my subdued demeanour. I've been feeling sad since morning because of a conversation I had with a friend of mine. His story made me realize how much our society can destroy one's life. Our society plays a critical role in shaping our characters and the way we respond to problems.

"As I mentioned in yesterday's lecture, we would discuss some relationship-related myths," James paused, taking a deep breath. "But in reality, we need to delve deeper into these myths. The myths I'm about to share with you are not just my thoughts; they result from extensive research and experimentation. Our community and society have instilled in us the belief that marriage is the solution to filling our inner emptiness as if it were the answer to all our relationship problems.

"We yearn for the joys of marriage, seeing it as a completion of ourselves. We envision our partners solely focused on us, willing to leave the rest of the world behind at our every beck and call. But how self-centred this outlook truly is," James mused, his words hanging in the stillness of the main hall at the Youth Club. "Our society has instilled these beliefs within us, never daring to delve deeper than our own desires and aspirations. But when expectations soar high and desires go unfulfilled, marriages can crumble. Marriage is not a mere contractual obligation but a spiritual covenant between two people," James continued, his voice warm like the pleasant breeze that swept over London during this time of year. "I am not here to accuse or fault anyone but to remind you of your responsibility in all your relationships, be it with your spouse, parents, siblings, friends, or children. We often disregard the significance of small gestures that can make a world of difference in relationships. And it is these small things that can trigger big problems. And now, I ask you this: What is the most crucial element for a happy and fulfilling married life?" James inquired, and his audience stopped writing, turning their undivided attention towards him, eager for the answer. "The key to a happy and successful marriage is cultivating a strong friendship between partners.

"This is not just my opinion, but it has been backed by research cited in the renowned marriage book, *The Seven Principles for Making Marriage Work*. A strong friendship fosters positivity and helps reduce conflicts that could otherwise spiral out of control," James said with a warm smile.

"As I've emphasized in my previous lectures on improving relationships, investing time in your partner is crucial in nurturing any relationship. The lack of quality time spent with your partner can lead to various issues," he added.

James continued, "Another factor that can create conflict in a relationship is focusing too much on financial matters. Money issues can put undue pressure on couples, leading to frequent arguments. Similarly, some couples are critical of each other's career choices, which can also cause friction."

The audience scribbled down these insights on their notepads, attentive to every word James spoke. He paused, then continued, "One more thing that can be detrimental to a relationship is forcing your partner to conform to your opinions, habits, and demands. At the Youth Club, we've stressed the importance of spirituality in relationships, and we've seen positive changes in many people. However, some still struggle with issues with their spouses and family members."

James locked eyes with the audience, and with a soft voice, he asked, "Do you know the reason behind these issues? After having deep discussions with these individuals, it became clear that they were all deeply devout and unwavering in their belief in the presence of a higher power and its role in their relationships. However, we also discovered that these individuals exhibited aggressive behaviour towards their partners and lacked communication skills and friendship.

"Their aggression stemmed from a desire to have their partners follow them in all religious activities, such as attending a mosque or church, reading religious texts, fasting, and more. While they had good intentions of creating godly relationships, they were instead forcing their partners to conform to their beliefs." James paused, and the room fell silent at the Youth Club. "The lesson here is that using force will always lead to resistance. It causes personality clashes, feelings of insignificance, discomfort, and sometimes even jealousy among couples."

He continued, "Additionally, there is a prevalent belief that marriage should be pursued solely for fulfilling anti-gender desires within religious norms. Unfortunately, this is the epitome of using a sacred act to fulfil selfish desires. Regrettably, our society has placed so much emphasis on marriage being the cornerstone of having sex and children that it has created an overly controlling generation. This disease of power control has caused significant problems in relationships, leading to issues such as narcissism and biased power dynamics. The problem isn't only in big decisions like moving or settling in different locations, but even basic choices like what to eat, wear, where to go, and who to visit. Partners under such pressure rarely have the power to make even the simplest of decisions."

James took a sip of water from the bottle on the dais, and the audience absorbed his words. "On the contrary, if we take a closer look at God's divine preferences for marriage, we will realize that it contradicts these social myths entirely. Our benevolent God has crafted marriage to be a relationship of sharing, where partners share beliefs, ideologies, powers, duties, and responsibilities equally. Neglecting these essential aspects can result in injustice, as we are denying our partners their rights," James' mellifluous voice resonated in the hall.

"Moreover, I want to share with you another thing that many individuals believe is a way to avoid conflicts in relationships — stonewalling. Have you ever been at the receiving end of stonewalling, or perhaps you're the one doing it to your partner? Take a moment to reflect on this. When was the last time you had a disagreement with someone and decided to avoid speaking to them for days instead of resolving the issue through communication? In my experience, most people realize that their partner is at fault but remain silent, fearing that addressing the issue could jeopardize their relationship. They believe remaining silent will resolve the situation, keeping calm and not hurting their partner's feelings. However, this act of stonewalling can result in many long-term problems," James emphasized with empathy.

"Stonewalling destroys relationships because communication is the foundation of any healthy relationship. Giving your partner the silent treatment and putting up a wall between you and them creates an unhealthy relationship where trust is broken. Some people use this technique to avoid accountability for their actions, while others do it to punish or control their partners. Although you may think that avoiding conflicts by not talking about them or ignoring the situation will help, you're only making things worse, and it distances you from your partner. Never go to bed angry," James advised with a warm smile.

James looked at the wall clock again, realizing it was time to conclude the topic. "In conclusion, you have learned marriage's true essence and significance. You are now aware of the actions that create distance in relationships with your partners and other people. To wrap up, I want to leave you with this thought: whether you are in love or in a relationship, remember that every relationship is sustained and remains productive under two pillars; friendship and forgiveness. Thank you for listening," James ended his lecture with grace.

James gracefully placed the microphone back onto the podium, basking in the warmth of the audience's gratitude. He received compliments and engaged in pleasant conversations with the attendees, but his heart was still heavy with concern for Brian. Despite this, he arrived home appearing relatively better, greeted by the joyful presence of Emma and Olivia. As he entered the living room, Emma's excitement was palpable as she ran towards him, her bright eyes fixated on her father's face. James lifted her up, showering her with kisses on her soft cheeks.

He sat down beside Olivia, beaming with contentment as Emma proudly showed him the scattered books on the mat.

James eagerly offered to help Emma with her reading, and the family settled into a state of peaceful happiness. Emma began reciting rhymes from her book, and James watched with immense love and admiration as she performed actions with her tiny hands. The stress and fatigue from the day's events dissipated as he immersed himself in the simple joy of watching his daughter learn and grow. Olivia, too, revelled in the moment, peeking from the kitchen with a sense of pride and gratitude at her loving family. She thanked God for the blessing of being married to James, who had transformed her life from one of hopelessness to one of gratitude. As he had once said, "Everything happens for a blessing."

As Emma's recitation ended, Olivia asked James if he was hungry, to which he replied that he was not very hungry. However, Olivia was unconvinced and began preparing dinner for her family, beaming with love and warmth towards her husband and daughter. Together, the family enjoyed the precious moments of joy and contentment that come from being surrounded by those you love.

Three days had passed, and James sat in the cosy guest room of Brian's house, surrounded by the warmth of the evening light. Brian picked up a biscuit from the plate, cradling a teacup in his hand. James appeared deep in thought, pondering something in his mind. "Take the tea, James," Brian urged him with a smile. James lifted the teacup and sipped it slowly.

"So, you're not feeling happy?" he asked with a concerned tone.

"I am happy, but not to that extent," Brian replied, his face downcast. "I feel like I'm at fault at every point in my relationships."

James listened patiently, taking another sip of his tea while observing Brian's demeanour. "Did you fight after your patch-up?" he inquired.

"No, we didn't. But there are some cases on which we are still contradicting," Brian confessed, sounding hopeless.

"Don't worry, Brian," James reassured him. "I told you before; it's almost like the start of your relationship again. You're getting to know each other and falling in love all over again. However, getting back to that level takes time because you both now think differently about relationships. You understand that, right?"

"Yes," Brian replied, sounding a bit more optimistic.

"That's why I'm saying it will take some time to make you both completely understand each other," James added.

Despite James' wise words, Brian's face still appeared downcast. James took another sip of his tea while carefully observing him.

"Listen, Brian, tell me one thing," James began, putting down his cup. "In the starting days of your reunion with Abijah, didn't you feel joy and contentment without any issue?"

"Yes, I did," Brian replied, nibbling on another biscuit.

"Brian, in the beginning, you were happy because your heart was filled with the excitement of new discoveries in the relationship. You were very focused and determined to save your life and relationship and prove yourself as the best father and husband. But with time, your motivation started to wane. And that's natural," James explained, patting Brian's shoulder.

"I'm happy that you haven't given up. Your concern shows me that you want to make your life beautiful. You don't have to be sad," James said, standing up from his seat and moving towards Brian's sofa. He sat down next to him and held his hand. "You've already taken the first step, which was the hardest one, and now you just have to take some small steps. So, don't be sad," James said with a smile, radiating positive energy. He was earnestly attempting to soothe Brian's nerves.

"Dear brother, I sincerely recommend seeking a marriage therapist's guidance and attending seminars on relationships, whether through my esteemed institution or elsewhere. It is crucial that you do so consistently to maintain your motivation. Diligently pursuing opportunities for self-improvement and relationship building will infuse your life with beauty and a profound sense of responsibility," he continued.

After a period of silence, Brian responded, "You're absolutely right! I must commit to attending lectures on a daily basis in order to remain focused on my personal growth."

"That's wonderful news! Your children will be exceedingly proud of you!" James exclaimed, offering Brian an encouraging pat on the back. "Thank you, brother. I don't know where I'd be without your guidance," Brian expressed, gratitude evident in his voice.

James embraced his friend tightly, determined to be a reliable support source. As they journeyed homeward, James felt a profound sense of elation. An indescribable contentment coursed through his veins as he gazed out the car window with a smile. At that moment, he offered a prayer of thanks to God for allowing him to be a source of inspiration to Brian and the opportunity to help him revitalize his family life.

"I am incredibly grateful that God chose me to help turn Brian's life around," James murmured, settling into bed for the night.

"We are all grateful to have you in our lives," Olivia responded sweetly, causing James to turn to her in surprise. Her countenance was warm and joyful as she added, "You are a true blessing to each and every one of us!"

James was momentarily struck, speechless, moved by her kind words. Olivia simply wished to express her admiration and appreciation for him, as Master Benaiah had taught in his lecture on giving compliments to uplift others.

On Sunday, the grand hall was once again illuminated with brilliant yellow and white lights as the first days of April ushered in a pleasant London spring. The refreshing breeze gently caressed the faces of James, Olivia, and Emma as they strolled along the pedestrian sidewalk towards the Youth Club, located a mere fifteen minutes from their home.

"James!" A voice called out from behind, and Olivia and James turned to see Brian rushing towards them. The breeze tousled his hair, and his face was lit up with excitement. James couldn't help but smile as he watched his friend approach with infectious enthusiasm.

"Helloooo!" James greeted him with equal cheerfulness, drawing out his words in playful delight.

"Hey!" Brian replied, his voice merry and upbeat. "I've decided to attend your lecture," he exclaimed, his decision made on the spur of the moment.

"That's fantastic!" James replied, beaming with pride.

"Where's Mia?" Emma inquired.

"She's not with me today, but I'll definitely bring her along next time, especially since I know you attend these lectures," Brian replied, patting Emma's head fondly.

"Alright!" Emma responded.

They resumed their walk along the pedestrian sidewalk, savouring the pleasant breeze of the April evening. In a matter of minutes, they arrived at the sparkling building of the Youth Club. The sight of the happy crowd milling about only fuelled Brian's excitement. He could see the excitement and joy reflected in their faces as they welcomed James into the hall. Brian watched as people rushed towards James, eager to greet him and receive a warm embrace.

James greeted each person with a genuine smile and without any trace of ego or self-importance. After a while, Brian sat with

James' family in the front row. James took the microphone and climbed onto the big stage, eliciting another round of applause from the audience. The smile never left James' face as he began to speak. For a moment, Brian felt transported back to his college days, attending lectures with a similar atmosphere but with a different set of people.

Brian took a deep breath and looked at James standing on the stage, preparing to deliver his lecture. "Welcome, everyone!" James exclaimed in an animated voice, immediately drawing the audience's attention. He held the microphone up to the audience, inviting their response. "So, what's the topic for today's lecture?" he inquired, looking out at the expectant faces before him.

James turned to gaze at the poster that adorned the back of the stage. Though he was well-versed in the topic, he aimed to captivate his audience with his words. "Dear friends, today's subject matter is rather delicate. We'll be discussing the art of handling conflicts in relationships. In our previous discussions, we've talked about the exquisite union of two beautiful minds, the bond of love and marriage, and the factors that can cause strife in intimate relationships. And now, we'll delve into the strategies and techniques for resolving conflicts in intimate relationships," James spoke while keeping his eyes locked on the audience.

"Listen, all of us who are either in a relationship or married know that conflicts are an unavoidable part of any relationship. And it's not just limited to humans; even animals engage in squabbles if they're in a relationship," James explained, barely able to suppress his amusement. The audience, including Brian, erupted into laughter at his words.

"I'm not joking," James chuckled as the crowd continued to giggle. "It's true, trust me," he said with a grin on his face. "In fact, let me share a personal observation with you," James added, hoping to regain their attention.

"About a week ago, I sat on the Youth Club's Park bench on a beautiful Sunday morning. The serene atmosphere and breathtaking nature were indeed mesmerizing. As I was inhaling the refreshing morning breeze, I noticed a pair of birds chirping nearby," James recounted, peering at the audience's beaming faces. "I'm pretty sure they were a married couple. The wife-bird kept screeching at the husband-bird, who was quietly listening. After a few minutes, the husband-bird began to shout as well. I sympathize with my husband-crow, who was the innocent one," James quipped, a broad smile on his lips. The crowd burst into laughter once again. "I was absolutely captivated by the delightful skirmish between those sweet little birds," James shared with a heart-warming smile.

"And through this story, I hope to illustrate that conflict and fighting are commonplace not just among us humans but among animals as well. The difference is that we have the power of intellect and a wealth of senses to help us navigate and minimize these conflicts in our relationships." As James spoke, the audience, including Brian and Olivia, was still beaming with laughter, enjoying his tale of the feathered friends.

"It truly is effortless to avoid conflicts in relationships," James continued with his charming demeanour. "Especially now that some of you understand the mystery and importance of relationships. With a few simple techniques, you can significantly reduce the chances of conflict with anyone and elevate the status of your relationships. But first, allow me to recommend something critical to those of you who are struggling with improving your relationships; mental food for relationships." James' warm gaze swept across the room as he addressed the audience.

"By mental food, I mean attending lectures or sessions to improve your relationship skills and reading books on self-improvement and conflict resolution. Without this crucial nourishment, your relationship's improvement plan may wither away. Therefore, I urge you all to read *The Seven Principles for Making Marriage Work* by John M. Gottman and Nan Silver. Moreover, I have ten more tips or tricks you can use," James added enthusiastically.

"Starting with the first and most significant point, prayer. Yes, prayer is the key to solving any problem. But often, we underestimate its importance. You will never suffer from any issue if you have a strong connection with your God. And the best part is that prayer is not just limited to relationships. If you want a religious partner, pray to God. If you want your spouse to love you more, pray to God. And if you want to strengthen your relationship with anyone or anything else, you can ask God for it through your unwavering faith in prayer." Once again, James' eloquent words held the audience spellbound in the main hall.

"The wise Steve Harvey once said, 'You have not because you ask not!' So, let us start asking God and watch our desires come into fusion. Secondly, listening to each other is paramount. As a lecturer, I have been forced to listen to my partner many times, and it has dawned on me that by actively listening to your partner, you can prevent numerous problems. Additionally, by listening, we demonstrate that we value the other person and are willing to strengthen our relationship with them." Brian was captivated by James' words, feeling as though James was speaking directly to him.

"Thirdly, it is crucial to identify the problem. It is imperative to understand what triggers your partner negatively, what topics they dislike discussing, and the reasons behind your arguments. However, to do so, you must listen to your partner." James' gaze shifted from the audience to Brian, and he beamed at him. "Fourthly, when discussing problems that cause conflict and distance between you and your partner, it is essential to have an open mind. There are two scenarios for this point: if you share your problem with a third person, find someone who is open-minded and unbiased. Do not engage someone who will worsen the situation by spreading negativity. Or, when talking to your partner, keep an open mind and be receptive to their suggestions and solutions."

Everyone in the audience was avidly taking notes of James' inspiring words. James' radiant smile lit up the room as he looked at Brian, whose attention was entirely on him. Brian couldn't help but smile back, knowing he had just received valuable lessons he could use in his relationship.

"The fifth point stresses the importance of refraining from playing the blame game, a common habit that can erode the foundation of any relationship. Instead of pointing fingers and criticising each other, it is crucial to accept responsibility for our own actions without causing humiliation or bringing up past mistakes. We must remember that our past experiences shape our decisions, and forgiveness should not be used as a tool to hold over someone's head in arguments. Using past mistakes against our partners can be demeaning and hurtful, leading to self-doubt and instability in a relationship."

James explained, "The sixth point is related to taking responsibility for our actions, which is a critical factor in maintaining a healthy relationship. Often, we fail to perform our roles efficiently, leading to misunderstandings and, ultimately, breakups. It is crucial to understand our responsibilities beyond everything else."

Upon hearing these words, Brian lets out an enthusiastic "Yes!" and takes a deep breath, ready to absorb the wisdom of the seventh point.

"Acknowledging when we are wrong can be one of the most challenging issues in any relationship, particularly in a society that is often biased towards one gender. However, accepting our faults is essential to avoid other significant issues that could have life-changing consequences or even cause loss of life. It is crucial to recognize that one partner should not hold power over the other and that both individuals should accept their faults without humiliating each other's dignity and respect.

"The eighth point emphasizes the power of apologizing and being sincere about it. Apologizing wholeheartedly can create immense value in a partner's heart and open a calm and conversational space for discussion, even when we are in the right. Remembering the importance of asking for forgiveness and admitting when we are wrong to maintain a healthy and fulfilling relationship is essential. So, start apologizing for even small mistakes, and you will notice a positive change in your relationships in no time," James said, addressing the audience with his kind and gentle tone.

Brian reflected on how many times he wanted to apologize but let his ego get in the way. "I wish we had more time," James said, checking the wall clock. "Moving on, the second to last point is about forgiveness. In my previous lecture, I emphasized that friendship and forgiveness are the key ingredients for a successful relationship. Forgiveness is truly the greatest thing. When you forgive your partner, you not only save your relationship but also your health indirectly."

James' words touched Brian's heart. He was grateful for attending this lecture and inspired by his friend's transformation. "The final point is to make a conscious decision to do better. Listen to your partner's perspective, make time for them, and communicate at a level that resonates with them. Apologize sincerely and forgive even if it's a repeated offence. Forgiveness is a daily practice that will strengthen your relationship and enrich your life. I understand it can be difficult, but pray to God for guidance and support, and you'll have a better chance of creating a fulfilling and healthy relationship.

"All the things I've discussed today will directly and positively impact your relationships. By taking one positive step daily, your relationship will gradually improve," James concluded the lecture. The audience, including Brian, gave James a standing ovation. Brian felt content, at ease, and determined to improve his relationship with Abijah.

As James approached Brian and Olivia, his infectious smile made him even more likeable. "How was the lecture?" James inquired with a warm smile, looking at Brian.

"Superb, brother!" Brian replied, beaming with delight.

James patted his shoulder, and the group, including Olivia and Emma, made their way out of the grand hall. "Come and have dinner with us!" James extended an invitation to Brian as he tried to rush towards his car.

"Thank you so much, brother," Brian responded with a sweet smile, "but Professor James just shared some valuable advice on dealing with conflict in relationships. So, I have to go and put it into practice." The group erupted in laughter, enjoying the light-hearted moment.

"That's good!" James replied, acknowledging Brian's commitment to self-improvement.

After Brian departed, James took a stroll along the pedestrian walkway with his family. The gentle, cold breeze brushed past them, creating a calming and serene atmosphere. "Brian enjoyed your lecture!" Olivia commented.

"That's wonderful to hear! I was delighted to see him attend," James replied, feeling a sense of accomplishment. Emma was sound asleep, resting comfortably on James' shoulder.

"All credit goes to your efforts in inspiring him to change his mindset," Olivia praised James, looking at him with admiration.

"Olivia, you always give me credit for things I don't even deserve," James protested with a soft chuckle.

Olivia widened her eyes and responded, "Why do you think you don't deserve the credit? You deserve much more than that!"

James couldn't help but smile at her kind words. "Thanks, Olivia. But all thanks and praises go to God. Even my life transformation was a great blessing," he said, expressing his gratitude.

James returned to the Youth Club the following morning and wandered through the building. A young gentleman approached him and greeted him politely, "Good morning, sir."

"Morning!" James replied with a warm smile.

"Sir, I have to talk about my issue. Can you guide me if you have time?" the young man asked.

"Of course, I have time. Feel free to share your concerns," James said, eager to offer his assistance. The two of them entered the cosy room at the club and settled onto the plush meditation mat. James turned to Kweku with a compassionate expression. "What seems to be troubling you, my friend?"

Kweku sighed deeply before responding. "I need to talk to someone before I do something I'll regret. My marriage is causing me a lot of distress and affecting my mental health. My wife doesn't seem to understand the toll it's taking on me, and I've tried everything to resolve our conflicts. But it's as if she's unwilling to work with me to find a solution." James listened attentively and didn't interrupt as Kweku poured out his heart. "I know you've given so many lectures on relationships, and I've tried to follow your advice, but nothing seems to be working. I just can't take the constant stress and arguments anymore, and it's taking a toll on me."

James reached out a hand and placed it gently on Kweku's shoulder. "What's your name, my friend?"

"I'm Kweku."

"Kweku, my dear friend," James said softly. "Sometimes, ending a relationship is the best solution. It's important to learn when to stay and when to walk away. May I ask you some questions?" Kweku nodded, grateful for James' calming presence.

"Is your partner treating you with kindness and respect?" James asked. In a heart-wrenching tone, Kweku shared with James his troubles in his relationship. His partner always points fingers at him for their struggles, blaming his low-income job and criticising the way he dresses, looks, and speaks. She even compares him unfavourably to her friend's husband, calling him a poor man without offering any solutions to their problems. Kweku has tried to improve their relationship, but his partner continues to taunt him for his financial inefficiency. Before, he was the sole breadwinner, but their relationship has turned sour ever since his partner started a high-income job and joined women's organisations.

"Perhaps your relationship needs more time," James suggested, hoping to offer some solace.

With a crestfallen expression, Kweku replied, "I have given her all the time she needs, sir. I try to spend time with her, leaving my work behind, but she doesn't want to sit with me. She would rather talk with her friends or spend hours on social media, watching one video after the next or chatting with strangers online."

Curious about the frequency of their arguments, James asked, "How often do you guys fight or argue?" Kweku couldn't give a precise number. He used to argue with his partner almost daily for trivial reasons, but after attending James' relationship workshops, he's tried to avoid confrontation. However, they don't talk much either, or there's no intimacy left in their relationship. Overcome with emotions, tears welled up in Kweku's eyes as he opened up to James. "Do you resort to violence during conflicts?" James asked, hoping that Kweku's partner was not physically harming him.

"No, but we did have physical altercations sometimes," Kweku admitted.

"Does your partner hit you during a conflict?" James probed further.

"Umm. She throws things, destroys property, and calls me awful names when angry. And yes, sometimes, she slaps and punches me," Kweku shared, his voice cracking with pain.

As Kweku revealed that his partner was a narcissist, James immediately showed his empathy by patting Kweku's shoulder and offering a comforting napkin from his pocket.

In a gentle tone, James advised Kweku not to remain in an abusive relationship, even if he had already made every effort to improve things. Sometimes, the most loving choice is to walk away so that both partners can understand each other's worth.

Kweku was understandably upset and teary-eyed, but James spoke from the heart, sharing his wisdom and experience. James emphasised that a healthy relationship requires a willingness to change, support, listen, take responsibility, apologise, and remain faithful. The relationship might be loveless and potentially dangerous if any of these vital components are missing.

Falling out of love is a natural phenomenon that happens to many couples, and there is no shame in admitting that the affection has ended. Holding on to a no longer viable relationship only prolongs the pain for all involved.

In cases where a couple has exhausted all efforts to reconcile, James suggested seeking the help of a marriage therapist. If that fails, seeking separation before anyone gets hurt might be the best option.

Sometimes, people get married to the wrong person for various reasons, but it's important to evaluate the situation and prioritise one's mental peace. Finally, James appealed to Kweku to consider the consequences of holding on to a loveless relationship.

By staying with the wrong person, one might be blocking their blessings of finding their soulmate. Holding on to a doomed relationship deprives not only oneself but also one's partner and potential soulmates of happiness. It's a significant decision affecting four people's destinies, and one should make it carefully.

Kweku sprang up from his seat, wrapping James in a tight embrace, tears streaming down his face. His heart felt shattered by James' words, but he was grateful for the wisdom he had received.

James soothed him with a gentle pat on his back and spoke words of comfort, "Everything will work itself out. It's important to let go of anything that no longer serves you, especially if it disrupts your inner peace. Remember, God has something better in store for you. Stay faithful and trust in Him. He always looks out for his children. Prayer has the power to change everything!" James said, his voice filled with warmth and hope.

Chapter Six

Maintaining my Individuality in a Relationship.

Discusses how God made every person unique. We have our own minds. Acceptance of each other's individuality. How to identify when you start losing your individuality in a relationship – giving in to your partner's every demand, inability to function on your own, How to regain your individuality

Chapter Six

Maintaining my Individuality
in a Relationship

As Abijah and her family approached the largest ZARA store in Westfield shopping mall, her heart fluttered with excitement. The dazzling lights emanating from the store created a mesmerising effect that seemed to draw her in. With her hands on the shopping cart, Jack sitting comfortably inside, and Brian holding Mia's hand, Abijah strode forward purposefully.

Mia, however, was starting to feel the fatigue from their earlier shopping spree. "Mom, slow down!" she pleaded, her energy levels dipping. Brian couldn't help but chuckle at the sight, admiring his wife's uncontainable enthusiasm for shopping. "Let her be, darling. Your mom is an avid shopaholic," he teased, barely able to keep a straight face.

Abijah's ears perked up at the remark, and she quickly spun around to confront him. "What did you say?" she demanded, her tone sharp and playful at the same time.

Sensing the opportunity to have fun with his daughter, Brian quickly intervened. "Oh, we were just discussing the meaning of the word 'shopaholic' with Mia here. Isn't that right, honey?" he grinned, nudging Mia playfully.

Mia's eyes lit up with mischief as she continued the ruse. "Yup!" she piped up, trying to look innocent.

Abijah couldn't help but chuckle at the sight of their playful banter. She playfully punched Brian's shoulder, admiring their teamwork. "You two are quite the pair!" she exclaimed; her heart filled with warmth.

The reflective glass doors shone brightly as they approached the store, beckoning them inside. Abijah couldn't wait to explore the different collections and discover new items to add to her wardrobe. Seeing other shopping enthusiasts moving from store to store only added to her excitement, making her feel like she was part of a vibrant community of fashion lovers.

Abijah glided towards the ladies' fashion store, her eyes sparkling with anticipation. "Come quickly!" she beckoned to Brian, urging him to pick up the pace.

Brian, feeling exhausted already, struggled to keep up with her pace. "Okay," he replied wearily, knowing he had to put in more effort to make their shopping trip enjoyable.

Abijah noticed his lack of enthusiasm and couldn't help but feel frustrated. "What's wrong with you?" she demanded, grinding her teeth in irritation.

"I'm coming," Brian replied, determined to put a smile on her face. First, however, he knew that he had to put in more effort to make their marriage work, which meant being more involved in the things that Abijah enjoyed.

Abijah held up a white t-shirt with Sheriff Woody's print in the centre, eager for Brian's opinion. "Look, how is this shirt?" she asked, holding it up for him to see.

"Nice!" Brian exclaimed, admiring the ZARA tag on the shirt.

Abijah then turned to show the shirt to Mia, who looked equally impressed. As Brian saw the ZARA tag, memories of their time in the United Arab Emirates flooded back, reminding him of a lady named Zara who lived in the hotel next to theirs. Abijah didn't like her, and Brian used to tease her about Zara. However, the name brought a smile to his face.

Abijah noticed his smile and inquired, "What happened?"

"Nothing," Brian replied, trying to hide his amusement. "I was just thinking about how people who love clothes from the ZARA brand would say, 'I love ZARA.'"

Abijah laughed at his playful comment, knowing he was trying to engage with her. Since their reunion, she had been trying her best to keep Brian entertained with her activities, hoping that it would strengthen their relationship. She couldn't tell if it was working yet, but for now, they were enjoying their time together, and that was all that mattered...

James' house was filled with a mouth-watering aroma of Jollof rice with chicken stew, making the air fragrant with the deliciousness of African cuisine. Olivia and Emma were in the kitchen, working their culinary magic to prepare a surprise dinner for James. Since their marriage, they shared the cooking duties, and James had introduced Olivia to the art of cooking African food, including his favourite dishes of potato leaves and cassava leaves. He would go to the Peckham Market to purchase his groceries for these dishes, reminiscent of the meals his mother would make for him back in Sierra Leone.

Olivia carefully lifted the lid from the pan, allowing the aroma of Jollof rice to waft through the air. Emma sat on a chair, engrossed in a food recipe book, *cooking with Mai: Easy-to-prepare-West African Food,* by Maimuna Zubairu-Burnette. Olivia, with a smile on her face, began to decorate the dish with a beautiful salad.

Soon, James entered the house, and the irresistible scent of food filled his senses. He knew that Olivia was in the kitchen, and after washing his hands, he went in to check. "Oh my God, I'm starving. And that smell, it's a familiar smell," James exclaimed.

Olivia smiled and announced, "Dinner is ready."

James kissed Emma's forehead and took a seat at the table. "What have you cooked?" he inquired; his eyes filled with curiosity.

Olivia sat down after placing the pan of Jollof rice on the table. "I've cooked Jollof rice with chicken stew. I wanted to surprise you," she said.

"Jollof rice?" James exclaimed, with excitement and sadness in his tone simultaneously.

"Yes," Olivia replied with a sweet smile. However, she couldn't help but notice the disappointment on James' face as he looked at his plate. "What's wrong, my love?" she asked with genuine concern.

James sighed, "Olivia, don't you know I dislike eating chicken?"

Olivia's eyes widened, "Oh, really?" she said, her voice dripping with honeyed sweetness. "Well, I want you to taste it for my sake," she insisted, placing the fragrant, crispy fried fish pan before him.

"No, Olivia!" James resisted, but Olivia wasn't about to take no for an answer.

"Alright," she said, still smiling. She opened the pan and showed the golden-brown fish to him, "Then take this fish. I know you too well!"

James looked at her, wondering if she was teasing him. "Are you teasing me?" he asked, his voice filled with amusement.

Olivia's smile widened, "Yes, it's okay!" she replied sweetly, happy to see James in a better mood.

"This was very thoughtful of you. I appreciate your love and cooking as my mother does. It tastes just the same way. I'm so blessed to have you as my wife, Olivia," James said, his eyes full of love and gratitude.

After dinner, James went to his bedroom and took a relaxing shower before settling into his bed. Olivia soon joined him, and as they laid side by side, James checked the calendar book on his study table.

"Oh, tomorrow is Saturday," he murmured contentedly. Excitedly, he turned to Olivia, "Tomorrow, we will go to Ndaha Clubhouse for a session!" he told her with a smile. "I am inviting Brian too," he added, picking up his phone and dialling Brian's number. "Hello, Brian!" James greeted his friend warmly.

"Hey! How are you?" Brian replied.

"I am good! And you?" James asked.

"I am good too!"

"What's going on?" James inquired.

"Thank God, everything is fine! We've just returned from a long family shopping trip," Brian said.

"Oh? A long family shopping trip!" James repeated, impressed. "That's great!" James added, genuinely happy for his friend. "Anyway, I called to inform you that tomorrow some members of the Youth Club and my family are attending a lecture on the *Acceptance of Each Other's Individuality*. So, you must come with Abijah, okay?" James said, his voice laced with enthusiasm.

"Tomorrow?" Brian asked, excited to join in on the fun.

"The session won't take long at all. It will only last an hour or so, and then we can enjoy a lovely dinner together," James explained, his voice filled with warmth and affection.

"I'll do my best to come," Brian responded.

"Come on, my friend. You promised me you'd attend last time. So don't let me down now," James playfully urged him on.

"Alright, alright. I'll be there," Brian relented.

"Excellent news! I can't wait to see you there," James replied, his smile beaming from ear to ear as he ended the call.

Olivia, who had been listening in on the conversation, asked inquisitively, "What did he say, my love?"

"He's coming," James replied, with a grin on his face…

James and Emma went to the park for a morning jog the following morning. Olivia stayed behind to prepare breakfast for the family. James playfully encouraged his daughter to run faster as they ran, teasing her with every step. Emma's ponytail swayed behind her, and she laughed as she tried to catch up with her dad. It was a beautiful September morning, and father and daughter were making the most of it, creating memories that would last a lifetime.

After their jog, they rested on the lush, green grass. The breeze was gentle, and the birds' singing filled the air. James looked over at Emma, who closed her eyes, trying to meditate and balance her breath after their run. Her lips were tightly pressed together, and James couldn't help but smile at her concentration.

"Emma, hold on a moment," he said, touching her head. "First, regulate your breathing by taking slow, deep breaths."

"Okay, Dad," Emma replied, her eyes still closed.

The sun was gracefully ascending over the horizon, painting the sky with a breathtaking array of amber and gold hues. Emma gazed in awe at the stunning vista before her, her heart swelling with admiration.

"Daddy, this view is so beautiful," Emma murmured, her eyes fixed on the sky.

"I couldn't agree more, my dear," her father replied, his gaze transfixed by the magnificent sunrise.

Father and daughter shared an unbreakable bond, a deep connection nurtured with great care. James had dedicated himself to raising Emma with tender guidance, instilling in her a sense of spiritual awareness and humility that would help her easily navigate the complexities of life.

As they returned home, the family gathered in the kitchen for breakfast, basking in the warmth and comfort of each other's company. Emma regaled her mother with stories from their morning walk, and everyone was contented. Yet, despite their idyllic family life, James sensed something was missing. He knew there was more to life than material comforts and yearned for something more profound.

Later that evening, James drove his family to the Ndaha Clubhouse, their destination for a meaningful session. Olivia dialled Abijah's number, and after a brief conversation, they learned that their friends were also on their way. As they arrived at the clubhouse, James felt a sense of excitement building within him. The prospect of discovering something profound and life-changing was tantalising, and he was eager to explore the possibilities with his loved ones by his side. "Where are the little ones?" James inquired of Abijah as they made their way into the grand hall of the club. "They're staying with my parents," she replied, her eyes darting around the bustling room.

Excitement bubbled up inside James as he gazed around the half-filled auditorium, looking at the eager faces of those gathered to hear the lecture. Emma was nestled beside Olivia, her eyes wide with wonder.

"You're not the one giving the lecture today?" Brian asked James. "No, my friend. Today, we have the privilege of hearing from one of my all-time favourite scholars," James replied, a hint of anticipation in his voice.

As the hall filled, Abijah found herself in awe of the vibrant energy pulsing through the crowd. "I have never been in such a crowded place before," Abijah said, looking at the audience.

Olivia, who had attended countless gatherings like this before, offered a reassuring smile and shared a fond memory of meeting James at one such lecture. "I have been attending such gatherings since I met James. I even met James in one of these lectures."

Seated in the front row, thanks to James' connections, the group waited patiently for the arrival of the esteemed scholar; finally, after about five minutes, the great scholar, Master Benaiah, appeared on the bright stage. Brian couldn't contain his excitement, turning to James with a look of wonder as the great man appeared on stage, "Master Benaiah!" James confirmed with a grin on his face. "J... James." He hesitated, as he couldn't speak for a while after seeing Master Benaiah in front of him.

"Yes, he is my favourite scholar," James said.

As the crowd erupted in applause, Master Benaiah beamed with gratitude, thanking the audience and the Youth Club team for their efforts in building such an excellent institute. The co-founder of the Youth Club, Mr Brown, offered his thanks to the esteemed scholar for his leadership, setting the stage for what promised to be a remarkable evening of learning and growth.

"Welcome, dear friends," Master Benaiah said warmly. "Today's discussion topic is near and dear to my heart: the acceptance of each other's individuality." He paused. "Reflecting on my journey to prepare for this session last night, my mind was scattered as I struggled to gather my thoughts. But then I stumbled upon a recorded lecture by the brilliant Mr James on 'The Combination of Two Minds.'"

As he looked over at James, a smile spread across his face. They met each other's gaze with gratitude and satisfaction. "His words resonated with me," he continued. "They touched my heart and soul. I couldn't help but be moved by his wisdom, and I knew I had to share it with you all."

James beamed with pride, and Brian patted him on the back, "Well done, bro!" congratulating him on his achievement.

He asked, "How many of you had the pleasure of hearing Mr James' lecture on 'The Combination of Two Minds'?" The majority of those in attendance raised their hands. It was a testament to James' talent and the topic's popularity. He couldn't help but feel elated.

"Well, that's fantastic!" he exclaimed, beaming with pride. "I won't spend too much time discussing the lecture itself because I believe James' words speak for themselves. They carry a message that must be heard in its purest form."

The audience applauded; their appreciation for Master Benaiah's humble approach echoed throughout the hall. "So, let's begin our session with a summary of Master James Tapia Kamara's lecture as our introduction," he continued. "Before discussing the acceptance and identification of individuality in our relationships, we must understand who we are. We must acknowledge the one universal truth of nature: that we are all different. Each of us possesses a unique intellect and uses it in our own way. We must embrace that God made each of us a completely distinct and unique identity."

The audience was captivated, hanging onto Master Benaiah's every word.

"As I delve deeper into this topic, I must share that even identical twins, born from the same womb, have distinct mindsets and brains. We are all so unique that our fingerprints are never the same; even those on our own hands differ from one another," he explained, observing the mesmerised expressions of his listeners.

"My point is this: if we are all so different, why do we expect our partners to understand our experiences completely? Why do we ask them to forget their identities and solely tend to our needs? Can we truly expect our partner to comprehend our every feeling, even though they have their own individuality?"

Today's seminar was a test for Abijah. The size of the gathering initially took her aback, and she now felt slightly disoriented by Master Benaiah's repetitive questioning. It felt as though he was directing his words specifically towards her. Her thoughts drifted to when she would confide in Brian, and he would struggle to grasp her perspective.

"Why do we constantly find fault in our significant others? Why can't we accept them for who they are? Why do we yearn for them to abandon their unique qualities to assimilate with our own? Why do we insist they conform to our beliefs and change their physical appearance to suit us? And lastly, why do we require them to completely transform who they are to suit our outlook on life? If you dissect every failed relationship, the reasons are often rooted in these very expectations," Master Benaiah concluded, pausing to let his words sink in.

The audience was engrossed in Master Benaiah's every word, scribbling down notes feverishly. Abijah turned to look at the faces beside her and saw that each one was captivated by the speaker's message. Yet, she felt suffocated, as if a weight had been placed upon her chest. She felt like a culprit, an offender to herself, while the rest of the room appeared joyful. No one seemed to be paying her any attention. Instead, all eyes were fixed upon the wise orator standing before them, and the truths about Abijah's character in relationships weighed heavily upon her. She longed to flee from the hall, but her legs felt rooted to the ground. For years, she had believed herself innocent in her relationships, convinced that she was always in the right. But Master Benaiah's words had shaken her to the core, his probing questions unsettling her soul. His words struck a chord deep within her.

"Is this what love and marriage are supposed to be about? Unfortunately, our society has twisted the meaning of a perfect marriage. We view marriage as a relationship in which our partner completely understands us, as having a servant. Forgive me for using such a harsh word, but if you look closely at your relationship, you may find that one or both of you are under pressure." He paused for effect and then asked again, "Is this the purpose of marriage?

"I won't go into further detail, for everything else is already in front of you. Our relationships suffer because we focus on transforming our partners to fit our desires, wishes, and mindsets rather than accepting them for who they truly are. We are quick to complain about our feelings, opinions, ideas, expectations, likes, and dislikes, yet we fail to take the time to understand those of our partners."

The hall was filled with an eerie silence as Master Benaiah's words sliced through Abijah's misconceptions about relationships like a sharp knife. She gazed at him with rapt attention, not wanting to miss a single word.

Master Benaiah turned his gaze towards the audience, his piercing eyes holding everyone in his spell. "And do you know what's even more damaging?" he asked, his voice filled with gravitas.

"The most insidious thing is believing that forcing our partner to conform to our views, opinions, likes, and dislikes is the key to a successful relationship. We pat ourselves on the back, thinking we're trying to keep the relationship alive. How preposterous!"

Abijah's breath caught in her chest, the weight of her emotions overwhelming her. She felt that time had come to a standstill, her surroundings fading away as Master Benaiah analysed her relationship with Brian. At that moment, she knew she had failed the test.

Her heart felt heavy, aching with pain threatening to break her. She longed to cry and release the turmoil, but even her tears had deserted her, leaving her parched and drained.

"I offer my sincerest apologies for our misunderstanding of marriage," Master Benaiah continued, his voice soothing and gentle. "Marriage is a beautiful bond of sharing, accepting, and appreciating each other's unique qualities. It requires growth

THE ASPECT OF RELATIONSHIPS

and mutual understanding, and those who fail to abide by these principles are not following the true rules."

Taking a sip of his water, Master Benaiah paused, his gaze kind and understanding. "It is a common misconception that God has ordained every marriage, but that is not always the case. Some individuals are too impatient to wait for God's timing and rush into relationships, hijacking their partner's life and affecting not just themselves but also their partner and their future soulmate. Let us strive to be patient and selfless in our pursuit of love, for only then can we find true happiness."

As Master Benaiah finished speaking, he turned to Master James and smiled, their shared wisdom and understanding shining in their eyes.

"Remember, dear ones, that a man's actions are often borne from his thoughts," Master Benaiah spoke softly, his words filled with wisdom and empathy. "It is why so many marriages crumble in our society today. Too many people are consumed with greed, selfishness, and wickedness, focused only on their desires and financial gains. Finding a partner who truly values and respects your thoughts, desires, and needs is a rare gift indeed. If you find such a person, hold onto them with all your might."

Abijah gripped the water bottle tightly, her fingers trembling with emotion. She tried to open the lid, but her nerves betrayed her. She didn't want anyone to see how devastated she felt, how she embodied the very selfishness that Master Benaiah had just warned against. But her distress was evident, and Brian's concerned gaze only made her feel worse. "Abijah, are you okay?"

he asked, his voice filled with worry. She couldn't respond, her body frozen with fear and shame. Brian rose from his seat and hurried towards her; his concern evident. Olivia and James followed suit, their expressions reflecting concern for their friend.

"James, we're stepping out for a moment," Brian said firmly, taking Abijah's trembling hand. "We'll come with you," Olivia and James replied in unison, their concern for their friend overriding any sense of decorum.

"No, it's okay!" Brian replied.

As they left the hall, Abijah could feel the eyes of everyone upon her, their scrutiny like a physical weight upon her shoulders. She wanted to disappear, to run away and hide from the judgment she felt was directed at her. But Brian's reassuring presence beside her kept her grounded, and she accepted the water bottle he offered, trying to steady her breathing and calm her nerves. But, unfortunately, Abijah's delicate lips could only handle one sip of the drink.

Concerned and worried, her husband asked, "What's wrong?" She remained silent, struggling to find the words to express what had just happened to her. Someone had just shattered the illusions she had been living under in their relationship. She couldn't bear to look her husband in the eyes, feeling ashamed of the role she had unknowingly played. "Abijah! Was it because of suffocation?" he probed once more.

Her only option was to nod, indicating that it was due to the suffocation. "I'm so sorry," he apologised earnestly.

Unable to articulate her thoughts, Abijah gazed at her husband's face, who had patiently listened to her words and promised to protect their family's future. She felt sorrow for him, for he was transforming himself entirely to preserve their relationship. Brian was puzzled by the way she widened her eyes in surprise. He took her hand and suggested, "Abijah, we should see a doctor."

Suddenly, his phone was interrupted, and he answered it promptly. "Brian, everything alright?" James inquired.

"Yes, James," he replied before opening the car door for Abijah. "We left due to suffocation."

"Okay, I will call later!" James hung up the phone.

Brian glanced at Abijah, noticing that she was recovering gradually. "Take some more water," he urged as she took another deep breath and sipped from the bottle.

"Brian!" she called out to him.

He turned to face her completely.

"I'm fine," she murmured.

He remained silent, watching her pale figure.

"I insist; let's return home," she suggested softly.

"Okay, I am taking you to your parent's house, and if you wish to come home, I will pick you up from there," Brian said reassuringly as he drove the car.

James and Olivia's worried expressions did not go unnoticed by Master Benaiah, who queried, "Is everything okay, Mr James?"

"Yes, sir!"

"Very well then. Let us continue," Master Benaiah replied softly, resuming his lecture.

"It is important not to lose yourself in a relationship. This topic is especially valuable for you, as the ones who control everything in your relationship. These points will help you recognise your weaknesses, and if you are unaware of yourself in a relationship, these points will aid you in realising that you are losing your sense of self."

The hall fell silent once more, except for a single individual in the audience whose heart and soul were shattered. Sitting in the crowd, the person listened to Master Benaiah with a broken heart.

"Through addressing countless couples in various countries, I have discovered that many individuals in our community are trapped in damaging and demanding relationships, devoid of any sense of individuality. If you find yourself fulfilling every demand of your partner without considering how it may affect your life and mental well-being, you are in the worst kind of relationship trap," he said. "Some people call it LOVE, but sorry to say, a sweet word should not be defamed by associating it with toxic relationships that have become more common recently. However, when one finds themselves tirelessly fulfilling their partner's demands without their choice, it is not a bond of love but rather a cage. Sadly, many people are in caged relationships without even realising it."

Master Benaiah paused and looked around the audience, inviting them to reflect on their relationships. "If your relationship doesn't allow for freedom," he continued, "then it is not a good relationship. No matter how you try to justify it, the lack of freedom will lead to difficulties in the future. How can you grow and flourish in a relationship if you don't have the freedom to express your opinions, ideas, and mindset? Who would be happy living in a cage or a prison?"

The chilly atmosphere in the hall seemed to intensify as if in agreement with Master Benaiah's words.

Kweku was in the audience and could feel the beads of sweat forming on his forehead.

"I've seen many people who live their lives catering to their partner's every demand," Master Benaiah continued. "Their whole existence revolves around fulfilling their partner's expectations. But let me tell you, this is not how to make your partner happy, and ultimately, these people end up feeling broken." Master Benaiah asked the audience, "Do you know what lesson we can learn from nature?" he asked. "We can learn about balance. Think about it, everything in the universe works in perfect symmetry, and this symmetry highlights the balanced nature of the world around us. For example, consider what you love; they all tend to be calm and balanced. For instance, you appreciate the symmetry of waves gently lapping against your body on the beach or the perfect temperature balance in a sunset scene."

The audience was captivated by Master Benaiah's words as he continued. "In a relationship, if you forget about yourself and work tirelessly to please your partner, you are acting against nature. Therefore, a relationship should be balanced. The point of balance is where the term 'sharing' truly beautifies a relationship. Sharing is an acronym for balance, which means accepting your partner's individuality without losing yourself."

Kweku sitting in the audience, had become a mere shadow of himself in his relationship, losing his unique identity to fulfil the demands of his partner. The memories of his attempts to revive his relationship brought him to tears as the coldness inside him intensified as he listened to Master Benaiah's teaching.

Master Benaiah spoke with empathy, understanding the struggles of those who cling to toxic relationships out of fear of loneliness. However, he encouraged them to see being single as a powerful state that grants the freedom to discover oneself, pursue passions, and make choices without limitations.

Kweku, who recently broke up with his wife, had been grappling with feelings of failure, constantly blaming himself for the relationship's demise. He didn't realise the positive impact of being alone and had forgotten the joy of living freely. As he sat in the audience, he chuckled at the relatability of the situation; he started crying, and tears ran down his cheek.

"Are you okay?" Master Benaiah asked, pausing to check on the emotional well-being of his listeners.

"Listen to me! If you have ever been in such a suppressive relationship, not doing the things you love, I urged you to reflect on your daily routines and identify the things you stopped doing because of your partner's moods or demands. You loved doing these things in the past, but you have stopped doing them. Why? Is it because you are afraid of your partner's mood? Raise your hands if you can relate?" Master Benaiah asked, looking at the audience. He reminded them that a healthy relationship allows for personal growth and individuality.

James longed to gaze at the sea of raised hands behind him, but he found himself captivated by Olivia's beauty as she also turned to look back. Memories of their recent dinner flooded his mind. It was one of Olivia's favourite dishes — a variety of roast dinners with chicken biryani and rice, prepared with love, which he had rejected. She could have raised her hand if she wanted. Her eyes could have given him away to the audience, but she chose to hold back and spare him the humiliation. The guilt weighed heavily on his heart as he observed her from the corner of his eye.

"There are plenty of raised hands; it means that you are in synchronisation with my words. Let me tell you another thing that most people say — although they love their partner, they feel unhappy and unfulfilled in their relationship. Maybe you sometimes feel that way in your relationship," Master Benaiah's voice reverberated through the grand hall of Ndaha Club House, and the crowd's reaction was palpable, a chorus of agreement with his words. Most audience members shared the common woes of being unhappy and unfulfilled in their relationships.

Someone's sitting in the middle of the audience amid this sea of emotions, his heart has been shattered, eyes brimming with tears and countless unanswered questions. He had come to the lecture hoping to find solace and strengthen his inner self, but it had only dredged up painful memories of losing himself in his relationship. He took a deep breath, waiting anxiously for the professor's next words.

Master Benaiah's voice grew more poignant as he spoke, "Your heart is filled with regrets, searching for answers in every corner." He posed a series of thought-provoking questions that urged introspection: "Have you ever truly been in love? Have you ever experienced what true love is? Are you in love with your partner? Is your partner in love with you? Do you know what it means to be in a healthy relationship with your partner? Do they reciprocate your feelings?"

Master Benaiah paused, looked at the audience with great emotion, and said, "My last words for you are, always take your relationship to God in prayer. Before you start any relationship, pray for God's intervention because you do not know the other person's intentions towards you. You see their face but not what is inside their heart. Some people are great pretenders until something triggers them, and boom, they explode. Don't rush into a relationship; take time to know your partner. Don't look at other people's relationships and wish for it; you're not in their shoes, so you don't know how they wear it. Looking from a window is completely different from feeling the texture. And never lose your individuality in any relationship. Thank you, everyone! Take care of yourself!" Master Benaiah said as he ended the lecture.

James felt a sense of relief and gratitude, thankful for the newfound clarity and wisdom imparted by the professor's words…

The auditorium began to empty as the audience dispersed, leaving Kweku with a tear-streaked face and blurred vision. He struggled to rise from his seat, feeling lost in the sea of motivated people exiting with renewed purpose. But unfortunately, he was the only one leaving with a heavy and demotivated heart after the motivational session, or so he thought.

As he walked unsteadily, the others around him chattered and giggled in small groups, discussing the lecture. However, he had no one to confide in, or maybe he didn't want to share his feelings. When one's heart is barren or lost, the bright colours and sounds of the world around them lose their lustre.

The lecture reminded him that he had lost his sense of self while striving to prove his worth in his relationship. Despite providing all the comforts he could, his wife betrayed him, leaving him miserable. As a result, he lost faith in people and felt worthless.

James noticed someone weeping on the bench across the road as he approached the car where Olivia and Emma were waiting. He could see the sorrow etched on the person's face from a distance.

"Come on, James!" Olivia implored, sensing his reluctance at the car door.

"My dear, please grant me a moment, for I shall be with you soon!" James exclaimed, dashing towards the other side of the road. Olivia admired him as he charged forward, holding back the oncoming traffic with his commanding hand gestures. The car horns blaring filled the air, causing Olivia to quiver with fear, yet her eyes remained fixed on James, praying fervently for his safety.

As James approached the person in distress, his eyes darted towards the forlorn figure slumped in exhaustion. Despite the noisy commotion around him, the person remained lost in their thoughts, tears streaming down their cheeks.

Finally reaching the footpath, James took a deep breath and drew near the desolate figure. With unwavering determination, he gently touched the person's shoulder. Slowly, the person turned their tear-soaked face towards James.

"Kweku!" James called out, his voice resonating with warmth and compassion.

At first, Kweku was unaware of his surroundings, but James' touch brought him back to the present moment. "Stand up!" James urged. Kweku remained transfixed, gazing at James with vacant eyes. Then, without a word, James grasped Kweku's shoulder and pulled him up, enfolding him in a tender embrace.

At that moment, James felt God had sent him to comfort Kweku.

Kweku began to sob uncontrollably, wrapping his entire body with profound sadness. James could feel Kweku's heart pounding with pain, yet he remained silent, allowing Kweku to pour out his heart.

As Kweku wept, James cradled him gently, patting his back with tender care. Although he did not know what had caused his immense grief, James was determined to help him through it, allowing him to weep until his heart was lightened. Kweku clung to James like a small child, finding solace in the warmth of his embrace.

He approached the iconic London double-decker bus 45 with a determined stride and climbed aboard. James knew that Kweku's self-worth had taken a hit, and he needed to help him understand his value. So, he prepared a powerful lecture during the week to assist him...

In the late-night hours, Abijah laid in bed, staring at the ceiling, unable to sleep. Her mind was consumed with thoughts of how she had stripped Brian of his individuality and the profound impact of Master Benaiah's lecture. Finally, she reflected on herself and asked, "What did I think of myself? Honestly, I don't even know. Even after our reunion, I kept complaining to God that he didn't understand me. I always wanted him to become what I wanted. So, why didn't I ever consider his individuality?"

These thoughts tormented her, and she couldn't shake them off. "How many times have I blamed Brian for his mistakes in front of God, my parents, and friends while I considered myself innocent? But in reality, I was the one who wanted him to change completely, according to my preferences, desires, and likes. And to top it off, my selfishness led me to believe that he was transforming into what I wanted him to become, and I was content with that," Abijah exclaimed.

Overwhelmed with guilt and frustration, Abijah grabbed her hair, trying to contain her emotions. Finally, unable to bear any more thoughts, she got up and opened the side table drawer, taking sleeping pills to help her sleep.

"I was forcing him to enjoy the things I loved! And the height of my selfishness believed that by imposing my habits on him, I was doing the best for our relationship," she muttered as she laid back on her bed, trying to find peace.

Her restless mind refused to let her drift into slumber. She squeezed her eyelids shut to force herself to sleep, but her thoughts kept swirling. Finally, she managed to drift off for a few fitful hours.

The Sunday morning was stunningly beautiful, with bright sunshine and a cool breeze that carried the scent of blooming flowers. But James couldn't shake off his worry about Kweku. The young man was in a dire situation, and James felt compelled to help him. The problem was he didn't know how to reach him. He only vaguely remembered meeting Kweku once and could not contact him unless he returned to the Youth Club.

Despite the uncertainty, James knew he had to act. If he didn't, Kweku could make a fatal mistake. Lost in thought, he was startled when Olivia entered the room and found him lying there, looking worried.

"James?" she called out.

THE ASPECT OF RELATIONSHIPS

He took a deep breath and sat up. "I'm just thinking about Kweku. He's in a bad way. I'm worried he might hurt himself if I don't do something soon. That poor guy is struggling."

Olivia nodded, understanding the gravity of the situation. "You're right. You need to talk to him again, maybe find out how you can help."

As she turned to leave, James called out to her. "Wait, Olivia."

She paused and turned back to look at him.

He took her hand, looking contrite. "I'm sorry," he said, meaning it.

Surprised, Olivia looked at him curiously. "What for?"

"I realised that I've been too controlling. From now on, I want you to have the freedom to choose what you want to eat, wear, and do. I don't want to limit you anymore."

Olivia couldn't help but laugh, amused and touched by his words.

With a twinkle in his eye, he gazed at Olivia's infectious laughter and asked, "My dear Olivia, why didn't you raise your hand when Master Benaiah asked, 'Show me your hands if you feel like you have lost your individuality?'"

Caught off guard, Olivia responded, "James, what makes you think I've lost my individuality in our relationship?"

Expressing deep regret, James replied, "The other night, I hurt you by saying that I hated chicken. I don't know why I said those things to you occasionally. But I am so sorry for my rudeness, and I promise it won't happen again. Moreover, I want you to know that you shouldn't feel obliged to attend my lectures because I deliver them. I don't want you to give up your life for me; I want you to do what makes you happy. Mrs Olivia Musu Kamara, I love you."

Amused, Olivia replied, "Oh, James, I adore it when you call me Musu, after your grandmother. I love you more."

With elation in his heart, James rose from his seat, embraced Olivia's head with his hands, and kissed her forehead gently.

At 11 o'clock, Abijah emerged from her shower, abstaining from breakfast. Entering the living room where her children and parents sat, her countenance was subdued, and her eyes were bloodshot from crying.

Concerned, her mother inquired, "What happened to you yesterday?"

Seated on the couch, Abijah responded, "Nothing, Mom. Didn't Brian tell you it was just suffocation?"

Hitherto silent about her emotions, Abijah was taken aback when her mother pressed her, "Abijah, please tell us the truth. What has Brian done to you this time?" Unfortunately, her mother was not in the mood to listen.

"Mama!" Abijah exclaimed, her voice brimming with emotion. "Please, listen to me, Mama," Abijah pleaded with her mother, who was visibly incensed. "Has Brian done anything wrong? I don't understand why he's changed so much."

"Abijah, darling, please calm down," Abijah's father interjected softly, his gaze filled with concern. He knew his daughter had finally come to her senses and hoped his wife would do the same. They had both been unfair to Brian.

"He hasn't done anything wrong to me. I've acted selfishly in our relationship. Please, don't say anything about him," Abijah implored her mother.

"Alright, let's go have breakfast," her father said, standing up and speaking gently to her as if she were a fragile porcelain doll.

The next day, Abijah returned to Brian, her energy levels visibly low. Brian wanted to apologise and ask questions but also to avoid conflict, so he remained silent.

"Perhaps it's due to her illness," he consoled himself.

Brian had informed Abijah that James delivered lectures every Saturday. She was eagerly anticipating his session and looking forward to Saturday morning.

James had also been in contact with Kweku, who, after sharing his life's tragedies with James in just two meetings during the week, was feeling much better.

The Youth Club building shone like a diamond in the sun on Saturday. A large number of people, including Kweku, had gathered in the main auditorium.

Brian had not yet returned from the office, and Abijah was waiting for him, standing near the house's main gate.

After a while, she called Brian.

"Where are you, Brian? I'm waiting for you!" she exclaimed. "I have to attend James' lecture!" she replied to his question. "What do you mean, we can't go there today?"

Brian was not in the mood for her to attend another gathering.

"Please pick me up from the house, or I'll call an Uber!" Abijah threatened.

Her ploy succeeded, and Brian arrived to pick her up within fifteen minutes. When she got into the car, Brian looked at her.

"Why are you so obstinate?" he asked.

Abijah's heart was already tender, and Brian's compliment landed like a heavy blow. Unable to articulate her pain, she remained silent, questioning if she was inadvertently pressuring him again. Brian could see the glistening tears in her eyes, and he grasped her hand tightly, offering a heartfelt apology for his misstep. Despite his sincere remorse, she couldn't bear to look at him, but he refused to let go of her hand, gently reassuring her until she relented with a soft, "It's okay."

During the drive to the lecture hall, Brian couldn't help but repeatedly glance at Abijah, worried about her fragile emotional state. Upon their arrival, they found James standing on the stage, patiently waiting for them in the lecture. Brian had informed him of their lateness, and James graciously delayed the start so they would take advantage of every moment. Upon seeing them settle beside Olivia and Emma, James greeted them warmly with a beaming smile.

"Last Saturday, I believe almost all of you attended an amazing session on identifying and accepting individuality in relationships. So, I believe you learned many things from Master Benaiah's lecture. My point is not to question you about what you learnt from his lecture because we are all learning daily from our past experiences, and the learning process never ends. I always learn something whenever I attend such sessions."

Today, the spell caster was James. Abijah was sitting in the first row again, and Kweku felt relaxed.

"So, as Master Benaiah said, his lecture was indeed for everyone, whether you or your partner are the dominant or suppressor. You must have assessed your life and relationship based on all his points and questions. Some of you might have found out that you were playing the role of the dominant one, and some are losing their individuality to their partner. Maybe some people will say that they have lost their identity altogether. According to all these results and findings, you may be thinking about the next step," James said, looking at the audience.

Surely, he is a person who stands on stage to address everything that possesses control of people's minds and thoughts. Now, I understand all his contributions towards our relationship. He is truly a powerful man, Abijah thought; she also wanted to know what to do next.

"The title of today's session is, 'How to regain your individuality.' If you or your partner should lose your individuality, the method is the same. The first step is to talk about the issues with your partner. Sometimes, we don't understand that we are actually snatching our partner's individuality from them. When you discuss this with your partner in clear terms and in a manner that both of you can understand, there is a greater chance that you can solve many of your problems," James said.

"You must tell your partner how you feel about your relationship. And, if you are the suppressor, You must chat with your spouse about your feelings and how you both can work on the relationship."

Why didn't Brian think about that? Another random thought came into Abijah's mind.

"And I believe that an understanding spouse will feel your pain and help solve the issue," James added.

Oh, I think I am not an understanding wife, Abijah thought with her face down.

She looked at him; he was sitting next to her. At that exact moment, Brian looked at her. Some seconds passed, and they silently turned toward James.

"So, now that you know your status in the relationship, try to maintain individuality. For this, you must make certain changes. You have to change your daily routine. You must either start adding things you love or eliminate habits that make you self-obsessed. As all the other scholars have said, a relationship is a bond of sharing. Start sharing your and your partner's habits by creating an atmosphere of freedom. You have to stay true to yourself and all your desires. Never allow your partner's happiness to come at the expense of yours.

Before changing your routine, write down your goals, dreams, and aspirations. Then write down everything you love to do before getting into a relationship with your spouse. Next, note down your dreams and aspirations and gradually add them to your daily routine. And, if you think that your partner is losing their individuality, support them by adding these things to their daily routine and helping them schedule time for themselves and their own quality spaces, which will help them maintain their individuality in the relationship."

The hall was silent as James continued to speak. His voice was firm yet gentle as he imparted his wisdom. "In a relationship, it's important to only participate in activities that truly interest you. Don't just do things to please your partner, be confident and assertive in setting personal boundaries. You can communicate your needs and wants in a respectful way that doesn't disrupt your partner's peace of mind or neglect your obligations to the relationship."

James gave a knowing look towards Brian before continuing.

"Saying no without feeling guilty is a skill that everyone should learn. You should also never neglect your friendships because of your partner. Maintaining balanced relationships with friends and family is essential in building your individuality. You deserve to have a good time with your loved ones without feeling guilty for excluding your partner. You should be able to have conversations and even your own separate bank account and spend your money however you like without your partner checking and questioning your every move."

As James spoke, Abijah couldn't help but feel a pang of guilt. She looked at him with unblinking eyes, taking in his words.

"Your relationship is not a one-way street where you must bow down to your partner's every whim. Instead, it should be a partnership built on mutual respect and love. Before expecting someone else to love you, you must first love and appreciate yourself. This is crucial to recognising and accepting the best that others have to offer. Regular self-evaluation is necessary for any relationship. You must ask yourself these important questions to ensure your relationship is fulfilling and satisfying. Is the relationship adding value to your life? Are you and your partner compatible? Do you share the same goals? What motivates you in this relationship? What are your expectations? Most importantly, where do you see yourself in three years?"

James paused for a moment before imparting some more valuable advice. First, he advised that talking to God can help ease any difficulties in your relationship. "Ask God for guidance and clarity if you struggle to approach your partner. Pray for strength and determination to provide your partner with the best while understanding and respecting your individuality. Remember the famous quote by *Steve Harvey*, 'You have not because you ask not!' So, keep asking God for help and support."

James looked towards Abijah and noted that he did not want her to feel down after the lecture. So he decided to keep it short and sweet, saying, "Thank you, everyone, for being here tonight, and thank you, Abijah, for joining us." The audience responded with a standing ovation, and Abijah felt empowered with a newfound strength to maintain her individuality in her relationship. It was a truly exhilarating feeling...

James returned home from his jog to a ringing phone the following morning. Olivia and Emma were with him, unable to discern the caller's identity. As they gathered around the breakfast table, James noticed multiple missed calls from Brian, causing him to feel a bit uneasy. He hastily returned the call, but Brian's line was busy. The wait for Brian's response was agonising, but around 10 am, James' phone rang with Brian's number.

"Hello!" James answered eagerly.

"Good morning!" Brian responded.

"Morning! I wasn't home earlier, so I missed your calls. Is everything okay?" James asked with impatience.

"What? Really!" James leapt from his bed, listening intently. "I told you it was possible, bro!"

They spoke for about thirty minutes, and James was beaming excitedly after the conversation ended. Brian had left James delighted by informing him about his conversation with Abijah...

Meanwhile, Brian was having a lovely morning meditating with Abijah and their children, despite Abijah's difficulty clearing her mind.

"Brian! I can't seem to quiet my thoughts!" she expressed helplessly.

"It takes time," Brian replied softly.

God was already bringing more beauty into their relationship. Within just a week, they had established a daily schedule to maintain individuality in their relationship, and Brian found Abijah's growing interest in spirituality very charming. Although Abijah struggled to keep her mind free from negativity, she consciously tried to play a positive role in their relationship. As Brian sat in the garden, he thanked God for transforming his life's journey.

"Brian! I couldn't do that!" Abijah exclaimed as she approached him, feeling defeated by her latest meditation attempt.

'Listen, Brian,' he recalled James' advice, 'now that Abijah is trying to act positively in the relationship, you must appreciate her efforts; otherwise, your relationship will deteriorate again.'

Brian smiled and encouraged her, "You are doing great! Now, you can meditate for 15 minutes with ease. I couldn't focus for more than 5 minutes when I was new to it."

Abijah's mood changed as they sat together on the bench. Brian continued to reflect on James' words, 'There are two pillars of a strong relationship; friendship and forgiveness. It's the only way you can create a strong bond.'

Brian leaned towards Abijah and said, "I have to tell you I am thrilled because you are putting in the effort. It makes me feel so happy."

Abijah smiled and leaned her head on his shoulder, feeling loved and appreciated.

'*Now, it's your responsibility to keep her happy because she's trying to improve just for you and the family,*' Brian reminded himself of James' advice and expressed his gratitude for his friend's wisdom. '*Oh God, how does that man know so much?*' he chuckled.

Chapter Seven

Building and Nurturing My Relationships with Others.

Discusses the importance of relationships with others around you, like your family, friends, and acquaintances. One should never neglect everyone else around them to be with their partner. It is a sign that the relationship with your spouse is unhealthy.

Relationship with parents

Relationship with children

Extended family

Good friends – better than pocket money

Don't replace God with your spouse.

Chapter Seven

Building and Nurturing My Relationships with Others

*T*he stunning sunset in the magnificent city of Bata, the former capital city of Equatorial Guinea, was a sight for locals and tourists alike. Positioned on the coast of Río Muni, Bata is renowned for its breathtaking beauty, and the sunset added an extra layer of charm to the city. On the beach of the Atlantic Ocean, people from all walks of life were mesmerised by the picturesque view, some capturing the moment on their cameras and mobile devices, while others simply stood in awe of God's creation.

Meanwhile, Carlos and Lucia were also basking in the glory of the setting sun as they watched from the large window of their house, which offered a stunning view of the beach. The glistening silver strands of Carlos' hair swayed gracefully in the cool ocean breeze while his searching eyes remained fixed on the view outside.

Carlos's face betrayed no hint of peace or contentment despite the sunset's tranquil ambience. For over four decades, he had stood in the same spot, at the same time, staring at the sunset. The room was sparsely furnished, with only a bed, dressing table, and an old sofa, reflecting the emptiness that had crept into their hearts.

Lucia, who sat on the sofa, pleaded with her husband, "Carlos, please stop staring at it." She appeared exhausted, with wrinkles etched on her face and dull eyes that spoke of her troubled life. The habit of her husband, Carlos, gazing at the sunset from the window was wearing on her nerves. She shut her eyes briefly, hoping to escape the vivid memories of their son and husband cherishing the stunning sunset and the beach view.

But the flashback made her tearful, and she swiftly opened her eyes to the empty room and dried her tears with a handkerchief lying on the bed.

Carlos took a deep breath and said, "Bella, see how our sun has set, but it wasn't as gorgeous as this."

"Carlos, you've repeated those words countless times. So why do you torture yourself by standing right in front of it?" Lucia replied, exasperated.

Carlos sighed and resumed his silent contemplation of the setting sun while Lucia looked on with a heavy heart...

In contrast, the Youth Club's building was bustling with the cool breeze of the morning as a group of people sitting on the grass in a small park, legs crossed in a specific position, practising Yoga and meditation. The fresh grass and the gentle breeze were calming their minds and spirits. The coach interrupted after a while, "Try to inhale positivity and exhale negativity," as a reminder. James stood at the front corner of the corridor, taking in the tranquil scene of synchronisation around him. The air was imbued with peaceful energy, and a smile spread across his face as he looked upon it all. Then, reluctantly, he realised he had to leave to retrieve more points for his lecture later that night.

As James made his way home, his thoughts drifted to the new members of the Youth Club. It was an achievement that filled him with pride. But, unfortunately, that morning, Emma was not with him because she was ill. In the past months, she became dull and less active after she started attending public school. Due to continuous fever and flu, the doctor examined her, but all the results returned negative. James had visited the school just to inquire if there was anything else that he needed to address; the school reassured him that absolutely nothing was wrong.

Upon arriving home, James found Emma still in bed. He asked her, "Emma, aren't you attending school today?" Tenderly, he kissed her head and tucked her blanket aside. Soon, Olivia entered the room to prepare Emma for the day. After breakfast, James dropped Emma off at school, and Olivia headed to her restaurant.

Though James was worried about Emma's health, the doctors had reassured him that it was simply the result of attending a new school. Nevertheless, he remained attentive to her needs, hoping she would recover quickly.

At night, the Youth Club's audience was waiting for James. Tonight, there were a few people at the club. They had arranged a small party in one of the halls of the Youth Club. Mentors, coaches, and friends of the coaches were enjoying the feast. James was reluctant to go on the stage that night. Instead, he was sitting on one of the chairs with his family, even though he was fully prepared for the lecture.

Brian and his family were also there, and James couldn't help but smile as he watched Abijah, eager to learn and attend the sessions every week, despite the difficulties she faced. "Abijah, mama, you're an inspiration to us all. Your commitment to attending every week, despite your challenges with gatherings, is truly admirable," James said.

"Thank you, James!" Abijah replied, although her gratitude was mixed with regret. She was trying to repair relationships and navigating it all was challenging.

Abijah softly asked, "Would you mind giving us a brief lecture tonight, even though we know you're enjoying the party?"

James smiled and replied, "Of course not. I wouldn't want to take away from anyone's enjoyment tonight with a lengthy session."

Kweku spoke up, expressing his admiration for James, "But sir, we could listen to you all day and night!"

The group laughed at Kweku's enthusiasm. Finally, James cleared his throat and began his lecture. After clearing his throat, James started the lecture, "So, looking at the great harmony between couples and families present there, I have only one topic to discuss. The topic of discussion is the importance of having relationships with family and friends in our life."

James stopped for a while and sat by placing one leg over the other.

"The reason behind selecting this topic is that I want you," James pointed toward the families and couples sitting around the round table, "to realise how beneficial your network and intimate relationship is to you!"

"I want to tell you that you are living a life of complete association and intimation, I think!"

James looked at them with questioning eyes. For a while, he could see the nodding heads of his friends.

"In that case, this lecture reminds you to grow your relationship with your family and friends. I know a lot of people who used to have strong friends and family connections but lost them after they got married. I guess it is because they became too focused on their relationship with their spouse. And, to tell you further, some of them also reduced time spent with their parents."

James stopped for a bit. Some of his friends at the table looked at him with naughty eyes, and some tried to relate to his words.

"And these changes are widespread in our society," James said, observing their connection.

"I'm not telling you a story about a couple who lives on another planet: these things happen in our daily life," James said.

The crowd started laughing at his comment.

"If you think it is hard to understand, think about your relationships for a few minutes. For example, do you spend the same time with your parents as you used to share before marriage? Do you spend time with your friends the same way you used to be around them before marriage?"

There was silence in the hall.

"Your answer will be no! There must be some exceptional cases, but I am just talking about majorities. So, you have also experienced that and become a bit busier after marriage because you have to extract time for your wife and children, too. In some cases, most people are cut off from their friend's circle and even sometimes from their close family circle. Sometimes they don't pick up their calls or even respond to text messages because they don't want to be bothered.

"You may have remembered that in my previous lectures, I talked about balance. Yes, maintaining balance is the only solution to keeping healthy relationships. God had made all of us in that way. He made us so that we always need people in our

THE ASPECT OF RELATIONSHIPS

life, either family members or friends, in distress and happiness. We need friends and family to live a better life by making every moment memorable. Friendship is essential to happiness and good mental health; it helps us relieve stress, prevents isolation and loneliness, it helps improve the quality of our life, but that can only happen when you have the right people around you because some friends are like Hollow Tree, they appear lovely from the outside but have a big hole on the inside which is killing them slowly," James explained.

"Your close and extended family members are essential for your well-being, as you know. Unfortunately, we cannot choose our family, but we can choose how we associate with them and what information we share regarding our personal lifestyle. On the other hand, we can choose whom we want as friends. Furthermore, we can't deny the importance of friends in our life; they are a great influence, and whether for good intentions or bad information, we need friends in our lives for a lesson or a reason. We learn from them, and we share intimate life experiences with them. So, as the famous saying goes, 'Show me your friends, and I will tell you exactly who you are.'

"I am a great supporter of having friends; however, you need to be aware of the kind of friendship you bring into your personal space. There are many reasons behind that strong belief of mine. The number one reason is that I still believe that some friendships are better than family members you have known your entire life. Think about this: if Brian hadn't come into my life, maybe we wouldn't be sitting here right now; maybe my life would've taken a different turn. Instead, I would be living a life of depression and competition," James said, pointing toward Brian, sitting next to Abijah.

Brian's eyes widened with surprise, and then he started smiling, looking at James.

"Further, I have been blessed with this gift from God, and I have used it to change the lives of many of my friends and my lovely wife. I met Olivia at one of my lectures, and we became friends after questioning my beliefs. Therefore, I highly appreciate and support everyone having a social circle. Otherwise, your life will be boring."

The wind was still blowing, but not with as great a speed. The atmosphere was very cosy, with the constant fragrance of BBQ that made James' words all the sweeter and more enjoyable to listen to. "Here is another thing that all of you should note," James said while sitting straight. "As I described to you the importance of having friends in your life or somehow forced you on having a friend circle, I don't mean to have thousands of friends," he added.

The small group of friends looked at him with unclear faces.

"It is not compulsory for you to shake hands with every person you meet. Neither is it meant for you to have hundreds and thousands of friends on social media about whom you don't know a single thing. Instead, telling you to have a good friend circle is to have a group of people who are honest with you. The group of people that know you completely. The group of people who are always ready to help you in every matter, and you can rely on no matter your circumstances."

There is another reason I am encouraging you to develop or maintain a social circle. It is because most people sincerely rely on a single person, and when the relationship breaks, they suffer. Why?

Kweku listened to his words with great calmness and got attentive to those sentences.

"It is because when that single person ends up leaving them, they do not have anyone else to share their tragedies with, and that can result in a devastating situation if care is not taken." Those words hit Kweku's heart directly. Because the same thing had happened to him, he had only one person to share everything with: his wife, and when his wife broke up with him, he had no one with whom he could talk because she had isolated him from everyone.

"That single person can be your spouse or girlfriend," James said.

Kweku put his face down by understanding his faults and thinking about his relationship again, but he didn't want to recall all the things again and again. So, he focused his mind on James' following words, "That's why I am encouraging everyone to have a social circle. It is because none of us are living a completely perfect life. We all have to face some challenges. Sometimes, we share these issues with our partners, but sometimes we can't, and we need to share these problems with someone else. For this reason, having a friend circle is essential for a happy and contented life!"

James' words were not making him feel ashamed. In contrast, he felt determined to correct his faults and all his past mistakes, which he had acknowledged.

"Moreover, when you have a friend circle, you remain entertained most of the time. This is because when multiple personalities accept each other in a group, everyone gets a chance to learn from each other. Let me explain it with an example. If you are feeling excited about something, the extrovert friend will make your moment more fantastic with his party animal nature, which is good for the soul.

"And whenever you feel broken or disturbed because of something, the introvert will listen to your needs with utmost care and empathy. Thus, having a robust social circle is paramount for personal growth and mental well-being. So now, let us all revel in this party," James concluded his speech with a smile.

Everyone savoured the delicious BBQ and relished the refreshing drinks. Emma was having a blast, playing with Mia and Jack, who had just started to walk. James watched his daughter having fun, feeling overjoyed and contented. *She looks so happy!* he thought, beaming with pride. Yet, as the night went on, James couldn't help but think about his daughter. He wondered what was going on with her lately.

After the end of the party, when Abijah reached home, she pondered James' words about building a strong bond with her parents. She realised it had been long since she talked to her parents. She felt remorseful about her last visit when she got angry with them for criticising Brian when she was at fault. "I should go and see them tomorrow," she resolved as she laid in bed...

Kweku, too, was ruminating over James' speech. He had just taken a refreshing shower and was about to hit the bed. He habitually goes over lectures before sleeping to absorb them thoroughly. "We need friends and family to make every moment of our lives sweeter," he reminisced about James' words. "Friends!" Kweku repeated the word, and suddenly, an idea popped into his mind. He sprang up from the bed and grabbed his phone from the dressing table. Then, with a stubborn look, he dialled someone's number. "Hello, dear Antonio! How are you doing, my friend?" Kweku greeted him with enthusiasm and warmth. "I'm doing alright, Kweku. How about you?" Antonio replied in his charming broken English, his voice filled with a hint of weariness.

"Listen, my friend, I remember you sharing some issues with me last week, and I've been thinking about you. I have a perfect solution that might help you," Kweku said, his voice radiating confidence and excitement. Antonio chuckled, and Kweku could feel his spirits lifting. "I am serious, my friend. It may seem like your problems can't be solved but trust me, they can be. So, when are you available to call me?" Kweku asked eagerly, not giving Antonio a chance to speak. There was a brief pause on the other side of the line, and Kweku grew concerned.

"Antonio?" he called out.

"I'm here, Kweku. I was just thinking about my appointments with the doctor," Antonio responded thoughtfully.

"When will you be free?" Kweku asked gently.

"I think I'll be free for an hour this coming Sunday. After that, I won't have any time," Antonio replied, sounding tired.

"Great! So, we can talk this Sunday, then. But you do not sound like your usual self. Are you alright, my friend?" Kweku asked, his voice laced with concern.

"I was just kidding, Kweku! Don't nibble at my brain any longer," he playfully scolded.

"Alright," Kweku playfully relented, his lips ceasing their teasing.

After their conversation, Kweku found himself lost in thought, with a smile forming as he reminisced about Antonio. "Ay Dios Mio!" he exclaimed, delighting in the Spanish words he had learned from his friend. Kweku had also picked up many Spanish words thanks to their friendship, but "Ay Dios Mio" held a special place in his heart. After a peaceful prayer, Kweku turned on his Alexa device and immersed himself in soul-stirring music. He sang along to VaShawn Mitchell's *Nobody Greater,* Sonnie Badu's *Baba,* and Timi Dakolo's *Everything (Amen).* As he laid in bed, his thoughts drifted to his friendship with Antonio. Since embarking on his spiritual therapy journey with James, Kweku had adopted a new outlook on life that freed him from worry and dependence on others. He had learned to cultivate a mindset that appreciated the freedom of life and didn't rely on others for his happiness. Kweku reflected on how, in the past, he would beg or chase after others to spend time with him, but now he realised that true friends would make time for him and create space for him in their lives. After attending James' lectures, many people started adding value to Kweku's life, and Antonio was one of the most significant. What surprised Kweku was that, for the first time, he had made a friend through social media, a stranger he had met on Facebook, who had become one of the most important people in his life.

On that day, as he waited for breakfast at Olivia's Restaurant, a place James had frequently mentioned in his lectures, Kweku scrolled through his social media feeds. Among the sea of posts, his attention was caught by one video, and his hands paused to watch it. The video captured a person indulging in their breakfast, relishing each bite and sharing the experience with the world. It was undoubtedly an extravagant display of their love for food. Kweku's eyes narrowed as he watched the video, disliking such attention-seeking behaviour. As it was a live video, he noticed another viewer reacting with an angry face emoji. "It's as if he thinks we've never eaten at a fancy restaurant before," Kweku read his comments.

The person didn't stop there. He commented again and again. It looked like he was taking revenge for something. Kweku was laughing, reading his comments. "I agree!" Kweku replied to one of his comments. He didn't want to fight with anyone or the video maker, especially not on social media. But his comments were so amazing and hilarious that he couldn't help replying to him. His every word was an excellent piece of joke. Then, he read his name, Antonio. That name was unique in the UK, so he searched for the meaning.

It was a Spanish name meaning "priceless one." By seeing likes and replies on every comment, Antonio got excited, as he had probably found someone who matched his feelings.

Kweku's breakfast arrived, and he started eating. He hadn't taken more than two bites when his mobile rang with a message tone. Chewing the bun in his mouth, he held the mobile phone in his other hand.

"Hey, what's up! I saw your reply to my comments, and I think we have the same taste and possibly the same values about life."

A message appeared on his mobile screen from that person, Antonio. Kweku smiled, looking at his text. Side by side, he was admiring his stalking ability. After completing the bite in his mouth, Kweku replied.

"Taste?"

Kweku knew what he was trying to say but intentionally asked about it.

"Yes, a taste of making such people aware of their B.S.," Antonio replied.

Kweku couldn't help laughing at his explanation.

Their friendship blossomed from the beginning, even though they were from different countries, cultures, languages, and possibly different races. They bonded over their love for humour and teasing, such as poking fun at those who shared mundane details of their daily life, like breakfast, lunch, dinner, or shower routine.

Their relationship was free from cultural and nationalistic biases, with their only common interest being their mutual enjoyment of mocking social media influencers' lives. Although Kweku didn't always comment, he gave Antonio unwavering moral support. Within just a few short months, their friendship deepened significantly. What started as a simple, light-hearted connection had evolved into something more meaningful. They supported each other through tough times, sharing their experiences of personal tragedy and failed relationships. Now, Antonio struggled with a brain tumour and kidney cancer, living alone and far from his parents. Kweku urged him to return to Equatorial Guinea to see his family, but Antonio was reluctant. However, following Kweku's attendance at numerous seminars at the Youth Club, his perspective on life had shifted. He believed that reconnecting with family was essential for a person's well-being. So, he encouraged Antonio to speak with James, hoping to change his mind…

Abijah confided in Brian the next day, sharing her feelings with him. He listened thoughtfully, then said, "You should go and meet them." Abijah was surprised by Brian's quick response and asked, "When will you be free?" "Umm… I can drop you there now and pick you up in the evening. Okay?" Brian replied. Abijah was thrilled and replied, "Yes!" Upon arriving at her parents' home, Abijah tightly embraced her mother. The two of them were overjoyed by her unexpected arrival. Abijah's father's eyes sparkled with delight as he beheld his daughter's radiant face. "Thank the heavens! My dear daughter looks beautiful and happy," he exclaimed, kissing her forehead. Her grandparents embraced Mia and Jack, showering them with love and affection. Abijah had avoided them for months, believing they disapproved of Brian due to her negative comments. She worried they wouldn't accept him now that she wanted to reconcile. "This is a lesson for me, never relay bad or negative things about your partner to your parents. Because even if you reconcile with your partner, you have already left a negative taste about them in your parents' mouths." However, seeing their joyous faces made her regret ignoring their calls and not contacting them. "I thought you were upset with me for supporting Brian and going home with him," Abijah confessed while seated on the sofa.

"Why would I be angry with you? I only want to see you happy," her mother replied, confused. Abijah rushed to hug her, overcome with emotion.

"I love you, and I'm sorry, Mom," she whispered. "I love you too, my dear. I only want the best for you and your family. Are you hungry? Let's eat!"

On a chilly February morning, Kweku prepared for work while sending a reminder text to Antonio about their meeting. He then headed to a café for breakfast and called James. After placing his order, James answered, sounding cheerful. "Good morning, sir!" Kweku greeted him. "Morning! How are you?" James asked warmly. "I'm good, sir. I apologise for calling this early, but I wanted to remind you about today's meeting with my friend, Antonio. Do you remember what I told you about him?" Kweku explained. "Yes, I do," James confirmed. "I'll come over in the evening, okay?" "Okay, fine." At precisely 5 pm, Kweku sat in James' living room, waiting for Antonio to join them via WhatsApp video call. Antonio appeared distressed, knowing James was known to lecture people about their lives. Finally, Kweku broke the awkward silence, "Hello, Antonio!" "Hey," Antonio responded, looking uneasy, with James sitting beside Kweku. "Hi, Antonio. I'm James. How are you?" James introduced himself politely. "I'm good," Antonio replied in broken English. "Kweku told me about you. Finally, today, I get the chance to talk to you!" James exclaimed. Antonio remained silent, unsure of what to say. "So, what do you do for a living?" James inquired, hoping to ease the tension. "I do multiple things. For example, I work at a car washing company and as a delivery boy for a local restaurant," Antonio replied, sounding uncomfortable. "Wow! You're such a hardworking person. But managing two jobs simultaneously is no easy feat," James complimented, and a smile formed on Antonio's face. James politely inquired, "If you don't mind, could you tell me about your hobbies?" Antonio responded with hesitation, "Umm… I have no special hobbies because my hectic schedule is tiring." James understood, "I'm sorry, you're right. It can be challenging to find time for hobbies with such a busy schedule." Having been informed of Antonio's illness by

Kweku, James expressed concern, "You should take care of your health. You don't seem very energetic to me. Is it because of the screen or something else?" Antonio remained silent. James then suggested, "Morning walks can be significant for the brain. Do you go on them?" Antonio replied, "No, I don't have the time." James insisted, "You should make time for yourself. Fresh air can help with your quick recovery." I am a patient with a brain tumour and kidney disease. I have an 8% chance of recovery. Do you think fresh air can heal me? James responded, "If you maintain a positive outlook, even a 1% chance can make a big difference." Antonio responded harshly, "I'm sorry, but I can't ignore the remaining 92%." Antonio's harsh attitude took Kweku aback, and he was going to end the call, but James stopped him. Then, with a surprised look, James asked, "What are you doing, Kweku?" Kweku, with reddened cheeks, replied, "Sir, he doesn't want to listen to you. At the very least, he should speak to you respectfully."

James comforted Kweku, "It's alright, Kweku. Antonio is struggling with his life right now." James then turned the laptop screen and gestured for Kweku to remain quiet. Antonio was moved by the situation and realised his harsh behaviour, "Sorry, I didn't mean to be rude to you." James kindly accepted Antonio's apology, "It's okay, brother. Where were we?" Antonio looked at James' calm face without any anger. My dear Antonio, you are already aware of the statistical odds that suggest your chances of recovery are limited to a mere 8%. That means there is a 92% chance that you may not be able to experience the life you had envisioned for yourself. Given these circumstances, why not return to your parents and create enchanting moments to cherish for a lifetime?"

When James posed this question, Antonio appeared tongue-tied and unable to speak for a while. Finally, he mumbled, "I don't want to return to them," while shaking his head. "Why not?" James inquired. "They don't need me. If they cared about me, they would have listened to me," Antonio replied despondently. "The truth is, my dear, they need you now more than ever. But even if you feel otherwise, you still need them in your life," James insisted, trying to encourage Antonio. However, Antonio remained unyielding. "I don't need them either," he said firmly. Despite his adamant declaration, James detected a certain fragility in Antonio's tone and questioned him. "If that's the case, why does your voice sound so broken?" A profound silence fell between them until James spoke again, urging Antonio to divulge what was holding him back from returning to his parents. "You don't know me, Mr. James! How can you expect me to return to them when they haven't contacted me?" Antonio's voice had shifted again, now laced with bitterness and resentment. "Fair point, but can you tell me what prevents you from returning to your parents?" James inquired, folding his hands over his chest. Antonio sighed and began to recount his tale of woe. "I was their only child, yet they never considered my wishes or desires before making decisions about my life. I protested vehemently when my father insisted, I marry his friend's daughter, but he wouldn't listen. His decision cost me my stake in the business, left me homeless, and ultimately resulted in my developing a brain tumour." Antonio paused to catch his breath before continuing, "Did my father not know me and my habits? Why did he do that to me? I now live in abject poverty without proper documentation, joy, or happiness. I exist only to count the remaining days of my life. All of this happened because of them. Moving abroad and starting a new life may seem like a dream come true, but it is a gruelling ordeal without proper documentation. Despite my education and background in Africa, without the necessary documentation, finding suitable housing can be difficult, even among friends or family. Sometimes, just finding a meal to eat can be a daunting task. I work odd hours in unfavourable weather conditions, often without medical coverage or insurance. People do not comprehend the hardships some of us face when trying to live overseas and make our families proud." Antonio's complexion appeared sallow as he spoke and seemed to struggle for breath. With his back straightened and a sense of purpose in his gaze, James leaned towards the laptop and spoke in a soothing voice. "Hmm, relax, Antonio. Take a sip of water," he said, offering a kind gesture. "Let me share my story with you," he continued, his voice warm and empathetic. "In my college years, I faced a situation much like yours. Though your background is likely more complex, I also felt a sense of resentment towards my parents. I blamed them for the hardships in my life, thinking that they had sent me away to another country without a second thought. London was like an entirely new world, and it was tough starting from scratch with no friends or connections. I had to juggle a part-time job and my studies just to make ends meet, and during all that, I stopped talking to my parents. I was angry, and all their words of advice fell on deaf ears. We didn't speak for three whole years." Kweku listened intently, hanging on to every word of his wise mentor's story. "But then, I had the chance to embark on a spiritual journey with various scholars, and over the course of six months to a year, I began to work on myself. Eventually, I found the courage to reconcile with my parents, and when I saw them again, I was struck by their fragile condition. Both seemed so much older and weaker than I remembered. My mother was even paralysed. I was moved to tears, realising just how much they needed me. But unfortunately, I had been so blinded by my resentment that I failed to see their suffering." James paused for a moment, his voice thick with emotion. Antonio and Kweku hung on his every word, listening intently. "When I asked my parents why they hadn't tried to contact me, their response shattered me. They had been too ashamed of their circumstances to reach out. They didn't have the means to travel to England, nor did they want to face me in their weakened state. All the while, I had been under the false impression that they didn't love me or sent me away to get rid of me. But the truth was that they had been suffering all along. My father had lost his job and had been imprisoned during a political upheaval. It was difficult for my family, and I had been blind to it all." James wiped away a tear, his eyes misty. Antonio's head hung low, clearly moved by the story. Antonio's companion implored him with heartfelt words, "If you believe that my circumstances differ from yours, please take a chance. Just this once, visit your parents' home and see how they fare." Antonio drew a deep breath, his eyes reddening with emotion. "When I returned to my parents," James continued, "I realised they were remorseful for their past actions. They recognised that I was too young when they sent me away. So often, our parents make poor choices, but that doesn't mean we should abandon them. No matter their wealth or success, they yearn for their children. We can't judge them for one mistake. Life means nothing without family. You should go and see them. The Bible instructs us to honour our parents to live long on this earth." Antonio's breathing quickened, tears welling up in his eyes. "You are an incredibly resilient and admirable man. I commend you, my dear friend. You have faced adversity with grace. But unfortunately, our ego cannot be worth losing our family. We may grow older, but we are still their children. I believe they await your return." "When will you visit them?" James asked eagerly. Two teardrops trickled down Antonio's cheeks as he replied, his voice trembling, "In a few months, perhaps, for I don't have the funds to travel presently." "No worries, my friend," James reassured him. "I am here for you." James didn't want Antonio to lose his composure. "Kweku, please send me all the necessary information for Antonio's visa and paperwork. Then, I'll handle everything," James said. Antonio remained silent, his head bowed in sadness. However, he was likely weeping silently. "I am undergoing chemotherapy and dialysis presently. How can I manage that in Africa? The doctors informed me I am on stage four with only months left to live, and they can't operate on my head anymore," he said with profound sadness etched on his face. "Prayers are the sweet nectar of hope that can change the course of things, and our faith keeps us going. Our Almighty

Father gave humans the wisdom to discover and develop medical treatments like chemotherapy and dialysis. We must have faith and remain strong, and trust that the universe will unfold as it should. I will keep in touch soon," James comforted Antonio before ending the call.

After Kweku departed for his house, James went into his bedroom; he sat on his bed, staring at the wall clock. The clock had just struck 11:11 at night. He took a deep breath and contemplated Antonio's plight. As he recalled his college years' tragedies, James grew emotional and started weeping. He wept uncontrollably for Antonio and his journey through life until he eventually fell asleep. Later, Olivia's voice snapped him out of his emotional reverie. His small family was waiting for him to join them at the dinner table. Olivia noticed James' lack of energy and asked about his meeting. "It went well," he replied. However, his slumped posture gave away his natural state of mind. Monday was a frigid day. James' windows were closed to keep out the cold. Suddenly, his eyes snapped open, and he bolted upright in bed. Olivia also woke up. "Are you okay?" she asked. James struggled to catch his breath. "I'm fine. It was just a dream," he finally managed to say. He ran his hands through his hair, trying to shake off the strange dream.

Olivia comforted James with tender words and a gentle embrace, "My love, it's okay. You don't need to dwell on the past." She nestled her head on his shoulder, feeling his pain like hers. James silently nodded in agreement, grateful for her presence and soothing touch. He had just awakened from a restless night, haunted by vivid and heart-breaking memories of his loved ones suffering in the hospital. He had seen the same scene that he had described to Antonio and Kweku last evening. Seeing his parents in that condition wasn't easy for him, and he also dreamt of Antonio in a hospital bed with the life-support machine and equipment all over him. It was a difficult dream, and he woke up crying and praying for God's intervention and mercy.

Meanwhile, Brian meditated with his family in the serene and picturesque garden, enjoying the fresh air and peaceful surroundings. As he opened his eyes, he caught sight of his children lost in deep contemplation, and a warm smile spread across his face. His laughter erupted uncontrollably as he witnessed his mischievous son, Jack, peeking through closed eyelids. Abijah and Mia joined in on the joyous laughter as they opened their eyes, amused by Jack's playful antics. "Oh my goodness, Jack! You startled me," Brian exclaimed, still chuckling. "You promised not to peek!" he playfully scolded his son. Jack, unapologetically, grinned and replied in his innocent voice, "Dad, you said no one would peek. But you cheated!" His sibling giggled in delight at his clever retort, and Brian couldn't help but beam with pride at his son's quick wit. "Ha! Caught me red-handed, huh?" Brian said, barely holding back his laughter. "Were you spying on me?" he teased, pulling Jack closer and planting a tender kiss on his forehead, feeling grateful for his loving family... With six months since his first conversation with James, Antonio was anxious as he packed his luggage. He carefully packed essential items and clothes into his backpack despite lingering doubts. He was about to embark on a daunting journey back to his childhood home in Equatorial Guinea, a place he had not visited in seventeen and a half years. As he made his way to the airport with James' support, memories of his parents flooded his mind. Boarding the aeroplane, Antonio's thoughts drifted to his parents' well-being without him. However, he reassured himself, "I know they will be fine." A stray negative thought tried to creep in, but he shook his head firmly, unwilling to let it take root. Then, looking outside the window, he saw the beautiful, soft white clouds. A faint smile appeared on his face as he recalled his and his father's shared love for parachuting in the clouds. Countless other memories swirled around in his mind, but he took a deep breath and closed his eyes, falling into a deep sleep for the long flight ahead. Upon arriving in Equatorial Guinea, the familiar sights and sounds greeted him. He took a moment to gather his courage, inhaling deeply before taking a taxi to his parent's home. He wandered through the picturesque streets of his homeland, taking in every sweet sight and sound. The soft sand of the beaches was strewn with families having the time of their lives, and he couldn't help but long to join in the cheerful bustle. His heart raced inexplicably as he made his way to his parent's home, though they were not his enemies. But reuniting can be challenging when bonds break, especially in his current state. As the evening fell over the quaint town, Antonio stood before his childhood home, gazing at the door with trepidation and hope. Finally, after setting down his luggage with the help of the kind taxi driver, he took a deep breath and knocked on the door. A few dwindling sunbeams peeked through the sky, signalling the approaching night. When a weak voice answered the door, he rang the bell again, unsure what to expect. Then, finally, a woman's voice responded, and the sound of shuffling feet grew louder. He strained to see who was coming to greet him, but it was an old lady who opened the door, her eyes red and wrinkled face crumpled with emotion. She gaped at him in disbelief, the stick in her hand falling to the ground. He quickly bent to pick it up, his heart aching at her fragile state. "Who's there, Bella?" a man's voice called from inside, and Antonio recognised it as Carlos, his father. But, when he stood up with a stick, Carlos froze in his tracks, unable to recognise his son. The years had turned his hair a silver-white, and his face was creased with age. "Antonio..." his mother uttered in a trembling voice, unable to contain her emotions any longer. Antonio stepped forward, enveloping his mother in a tight embrace. She clung to his shirt, weeping uncontrollably as tears streamed down his face. He then turned to his father, who leaned against the wall, silently weeping. With his other hand, Antonio reached out, his palm open and waiting for his father's touch. The three of them wept together, holding each other tightly. Antonio was their only child, and it had been nearly 18 years since they had seen him. Those years had been filled with endless sorrow and grief as they were unsure if their son was still alive. They had lost him by forcing their desires on him, and not a day had passed when Carlos didn't curse himself for it. The long years had taken everything from them, robbing them of the ability to enjoy life. Their daily routine consisted of watching the sunset while standing by the door or window, and every night, they slept in extreme misery. They had stopped hoping for Antonio's return, and it seemed as though nature had finally heard their prayers...

In London, the evening was peaceful as James sat in his living room, sipping tea. Then, suddenly, he received a call from Antonio. "Hello, man! How are you?" James asked, smiling. Antonio replied, "Hey! I'm fine! I just wanted to say thank you!"

James inquired about Antonio's parents, and the young man replied with a broken voice, expressing how happy they were to reunite after so many years of separation finally. However, he lamented that he wished James had come into his life earlier, as his parents had been waiting and counting the days for his return. James reassured him that it was never too late to make amends, and he was pleased that Antonio realised the importance of his parents before it was too late. Antonio expressed his guilt for the pain he had caused his parents, but James encouraged him to focus on the present and the opportunity to make things right. With gratitude and determination, Antonio promised to visit the hospital the following morning, as James had arranged with the doctor. "Good! Now, spend time with your parents and don't forget to visit the hospital tomorrow morning. The doctor is expecting you. I spoke with her yesterday. Bye!" James said.

"Bye, and thanks once again. I will definitely make the trip to the hospital in the morning!"

After the call ended, James observed Emma eating biscuits with her mother. He couldn't help but feel anxious about her health and the missing piece of their parenting that may have contributed to her illness. Olivia reminded James of Emma's medical reports, and he promised to retrieve them from the doctor soon. Despite the joy of Antonio's reunion with his parents, James remained attentive to his family's needs, determined to provide them with the care and attention they deserved. With a determined look, James arrived at the hospital and eagerly discussed Emma's condition with Dr Sam, who was not only a professional but also a trusted friend. The medical reports revealed no major concerns, but Dr Sam knew James well enough to understand something else was amiss. "James, these reports are not giving us any useful information," Dr Sam said while gesturing towards the files. "But I've noticed something about Emma's behaviour that could help her." James leaned in, listening intently to the doctor's every word. "She needs a companion," Dr Sam declared. "I'm always there for her," James replied. "I listen to her and take her to places she loves." "You're doing great, James, but perhaps we need to explore other options, like physical medication," Dr Sam suggested. James took a deep breath, pondering the doctor's words. "Don't worry, James. Everything will be fine," Dr Sam reassured him. "But how can I provide her with more company? We only have time at night, and that's when she sleeps," James said, his voice full of concern. After thinking for a while, Dr Sam had an idea. "It might be best to leave Emma with a friend for a day or two." "Okay, I will consider that," James replied. James pondered his daily schedule as he walked out of the clinic, clutching the medical files in his hand. *Dr Sam is right. We need to spend more quality time together like we used to,* James thought. *I need to figure out a way to remedy this situation.*

As James arrived home, he found Emma fast asleep. He immediately confided in Olivia, sharing all the details Dr Sam gave him. But upon hearing the news, Olivia grew anxious. "James, do you have any ideas on what to do?" Olivia asked. "Nothing yet," replied James. Filled with thoughts, doubts, and worries about Emma's health, James struggled to fall asleep that night. The next morning, he awoke with a start after having another dream of his parents. Concerned, Olivia suggested he speak with them and see if it could help alleviate his anxiety. "Hmm," murmured James. He spent the rest of the day deep in thought, wondering what God was trying to tell him. Finally, he turned to prayer, asking for guidance and direction. Two nights later, James stood at the door, saying his goodbyes to Emma and Olivia before embarking on his journey. Olivia was surprised by his sudden decision, but she kept herself busy with Emma in his absence. As evening approached, James had not yet contacted Olivia to let her know he arrived safely. She anxiously checked her phone, waiting for any news. Finally, at 10 p.m., her phone rang. "How was your trip back home?" she asked. "It was great, my love," James replied. "The journey from Lungi International Airport to Freetown was quite a struggle. Our ferry had trouble mid-sea, and once we arrived at the ferry terminal in Kissy, the traffic to Lakka village was a nightmare. But when I finally arrived home, my parents were attending my cousin's traditional wedding ceremony. So they were surprised to see me there!" "What a delightful surprise! Please give my warm regards to everyone, and I'm glad you made it home safely. When is your appointment at the embassy?" Olivia inquired. "We have it scheduled for Tuesday. If all goes well, we should be back by Thursday," James responded. "By God's grace. Please take care of yourself and stay safe. I love you," Olivia said, relieved to hear from him.

With a heart full of affection, James ended the call by saying, "I love you more, Mrs Kamara, and kiss Emma good night for me." Finally, the long-awaited day arrived. On Tuesday morning, James and his parents visited the British High Commissioner in Spur Road, Freetown, Sierra Leone. They had an appointment at 10:30 am, and by 2 pm, they received their visiting visas. Even though Mr Bai Kamara and Mrs Fatu Oyah Kamara had visited the UK before, this time was special because their son had sponsored their trip and applied for their visas. They were overwhelmed with joy and excitement.

Four days later, a cheerful ring of the doorbell echoed through the house, drawing Olivia's attention. With a wide grin illuminating her face, she swung open the door, revealing James and his parents standing on the doorstep. Filled with warmth, Olivia joyfully welcomed them inside. Emma's heart swelled with delight upon seeing her beloved grandparents, and the hours melted away as they immersed themselves in heartfelt conversations. James and Olivia nestled beside them, enveloped in the tender affection that enveloped their close-knit family.

A moment brimming with anticipation unfurled as Emma's grandparents extended a gift box to her. Within its humble confines lay a treasure trove of delights — a collection of vibrant African dresses that whispered of distant lands, a delectable

Bennie cake adorned with sesame seeds, a mouthwatering Granat cake infused with the rich essence of peanuts, and a jar of Kayan, a delightful blend of rice powder and creamy peanut butter. Nestled among these delights, lay a book, poised to transport Emma's imagination to wondrous realms.

Bubbling over with excitement, Emma eagerly peeled open the book's cover, immersing herself in its pages. Her voice danced with joy as she read aloud to her attentive grandparents, lost in the enchanting tale of *Adama Loves Akara*, a heartwarming story penned by Vickie Remoe. Turning to her grandma, Emma's eyes sparkled with gratitude as she expressed her heartfelt sentiments, "Grandma, I caught sight of Vickie Remoe on Facebook, where she spoke passionately about her book. Papa allowed me to watch her video, promising to purchase this treasure for me, but alas, it slipped away like a fleeting dream. Thank you, Grandma, for making it a reality. I love you so much." As they talked, James reflected on the importance of family and strong bonds with immediate and extended family members. "We must never forget how much our parents mean to us," he said. "They raised us, cared for us, and gave us everything they had. We must make time for them, show them respect, forgiveness, and most importantly, love." He reached for Olivia's hand and said, "I wish we could find your mother one day, my love. I would love to thank her for giving birth to this beautiful soul I call my wife." Olivia's eyes sparkled with tears of happiness as she replied, "It's possible one day, my love. I believe it's possible." James gazed lovingly at her and said, "I love you more and more each day, and

I will forever cherish you." The tiny house was again filled with joy, love, and laughter as the family spent the evening together, creating beautiful memories to last a lifetime.

Chapter Eight

The Father and Son Relationship

Discuss the importance of a father in his son's life.

The difference between Dad's love and Mom's love

Boys want to be like Dad.

Discuss the relationship in childhood vs adolescence vs adulthood.

*Common relationship problems between father and son –
Communication, lifestyle choices, sexual proclivities, household
standards*

*Fixing conflict between father and son – better communication,
understanding each other, mutual respect, finding common ground,
spending quality time together, don't shy away from sensitive topics,
celebrating accomplishments.*

The Father and Son Relationship

Carlos and Antonio stood side by side, gazing out the window at the breathtaking sunset, which had turned the city of Bata into a tourist's paradise. The refreshing breeze caressed their faces, bringing peace and tranquillity to their hearts. Antonio couldn't help but sneak a glance at his father, who stood beside him with a warm smile. There was something so captivating about Carlos' smile that Antonio found himself unable to look away. As he studied his father's face, he noticed a hint of moisture in the corner of his eyes. Sensing his son's gaze, Carlos gently shook his head and beamed at him.

"I love this stunning sunset! It's just gorgeous, don't you think?" Carlos exclaimed, his eyes twinkling with joy.

Antonio nodded in agreement, unable to tear his eyes away from his father's face. He knew that Carlos was hiding something, as he often did. Antonio and his mother were aware of his father's love for sunsets, but they also knew something else made this sunset scene special for Carlos. "Are you crying, Dad?" Antonio asked, his tone filled with suspicion.

"What? Crying?" Carlos quickly composed himself, his expression turning serious. "No, Antonio. I'm not crying."

Despite Carlos' reassurances, Antonio could see the doubt in his father's eyes. He chose not to push the matter and simply smiled, taking a deep breath to savour the beauty of the moment. Carlos couldn't bear the scrutiny any longer, so he playfully punched Antonio's arm and chuckled. "Hey, stop staring at me like that, young man!" he teased, his eyes shining with love and affection for his son.

Carlos had left the window and retreated to his bed, clutching the newspaper tightly in his hand. He had been reading it earlier that morning, but now he was hiding something behind its pages. Antonio couldn't help but smile at his father's attempt to conceal his emotions. He wanted to say and ask many things, but the words seemed to escape him. He turned back towards the window, watching as the last remnants of the sunset faded away, making way for the encroaching darkness.

Since he left, it seemed like someone had stolen the words from his mouth. Antonio could hardly believe his departure had left his parents so lost and adrift. He never could have imagined his father in such a state. Carlos was always the epitome of elegance and refinement, a strict disciplinarian who adhered strictly to rules and regulations. He was health-conscious and maybe even beauty-conscious and was the fittest man of his age in the community. But within a few short years, everything had changed. The wrinkles on his father's face, his white hair, and his simple lifestyle were all tell-tale signs of ageing. It was as if the burden of losing his only son had aged him beyond his years. He had lost his sense of purpose, health, and even his zest for life. The house that used to be filled with an array of accessories now stood almost empty. Carlos had given away all of Antonio's belongings to their neighbours, unable to bear the constant reminder of his absence. There were no pictures on the walls, no signs of life in the once-vibrant home. Carlos had lost everything.

Life had unfurled a new chapter in front of him, one that was centred around the boundless love of a father. As an only child, he had always been closely connected with his mother, just like other kids. However, though he had spent time playing with his father, there was always a distance between them, lacking the ease and camaraderie he shared with his mother. Occasionally, his father's stern demeanour had even caused his offence.

As he prepared to leave home, he knew that his mother would miss him dearly, but it never occurred to him that his father would be equally devastated by his departure. Upon his return, he was stunned to see his father in tears. Since his arrival, his father had not demanded anything of him, unlike before, and his words were kind and gentle. There was a newfound tranquillity in his father's demeanour, which was unfamiliar to him but not to his mother, who had known Carlos since their marriage.

"Dad has changed so much, hasn't he?" he asked his mother, Bella, as he rested his head on her lap. "No, he hasn't changed at all," Bella replied with a deep breath. "He has always been loving and kind, haven't I told you before? But look at what your separation has done to him. Only God knows how I managed to handle Carlos all this while. It wasn't easy for him. He took it very hard."

Bella was aware of the real intent behind Antonio's question, and thus she wanted to reinforce his father's love for him. So, with an affectionate pat on his head, she said, "Dads are tough to understand, but never doubt their love, and your papa loves you more than you can imagine!" And she was right. As Antonio closed his eyes, he could feel the wetness in the corner of his father's eyes, confirming his mother's words.

"Antonio, my dear son, I can't help but notice these scars on your head. Since you returned from Spain, you've been coming and going from the house, and you don't seem like the same person I bid farewell to. You look so fragile, like you've been deprived of food for ages. I even saw you taking medications the other day. Is it because of the divorce with Ezabella that you're feeling this way, or is something else bothering you? Please talk to me; my heart is restless with worry. I can't stop thinking about it ever since you arrived," Bella expressed with a quiver in her voice, her eyes filled with concern.

"Mom, it's not easy to tell you this, but I must let you know since you're concerned. First, however, please promise me that you won't tell Papa until I'm ready," Antonio said, sitting upright and locking his gaze with his mother's.

"In life, we all have a purpose to fulfil, a legacy to leave behind. In my case, the doctors have given me only 36 years to fulfil it," Antonio revealed, and Bella's face instantly changed with shock and disbelief, trying to comprehend what her son was telling her.

"I have accepted my fate and am content with God's plans for my life. But I can't leave this world without seeing you and Papa one last time. I need to make amends and feel that parental love one more time," Antonio continued with a soft and gentle tone.

Bella's heart sank, and she felt like her soul was being sucked out of her body as she listened to her son's words. She didn't know whether to scream or flee from the world. All she could think of was holding her son tightly and never letting go.

The scars adorning my head tell a story of my eight-year battle with a brain tumour. Since returning home, I've been in and out of your house, going to the hospital arranged and funded by my dear friend James from England. Here in Bata, I'm starting my chemotherapy for my kidney cancer, hoping to return to Spain when the time is right.

As Bella held her son tightly, tears streamed down her face, unable to fathom the news of her only child's illness. "Antonio, you've killed me. What is this I am hearing about my only child? God, why are you doing this to me? Why my son? Why does it have to be my child? You're only 36 years old and have lots of fun times awaiting you. You haven't even given me grandchildren yet. Antonio, this cannot be true. The doctors are not God. The God I serve will never do this to me. Antonio, Antonio, Antonio, Antonio, my son, Antonio, my life. Now that I found my son, God, please stop all this and tell me I am only dreaming," in her native tongue, she cried out to the heavens, begging for this to be a terrible nightmare.

Bella's grip on her son tightened as if he would disappear if she let go. Antonio's eyes filled with tears, realising the pain and anguish he had caused his mother. He continued to share his journey with her, filled with remorse and regret. As he concluded, she asked, "My son, do they need my kidney to do a transplant for you? Your dad and I will willingly give you ours. If they need any of our body parts, please collect them, so you can get better. Is that why you're here, so I can give you my kidney? Please, my son, let's go to the hospital so they can make you better," Bella cried out. "We'll do whatever it takes to make you better."

Sadly, the doctors had informed Antonio that it was too late for a transplant. "Mama, according to my doctors in Spain and here in Bata, it's too late for all that. It was discovered late, and I am already in the final stages with only six months to live. However, they said it might be longer with the help of chemotherapy and medications. Please, I want those six months to be the best of my life if possible. I need you guys now more than ever. I need to feel the love around me and see the beautiful sunset of our planet."

Bella continued crying and praying to God for his divine intervention.

"Please don't tell Papa until I tell him, please, Mama," Bella nodded in reassurance while wailing in tears and praying for God's intervention...

Meanwhile, Brian and his four-year-old son, Jack, were having the time of their lives, running and laughing in the nearby park, Abijah, capturing every moment on film. His four years old son was enjoying the best moments of his life with his father. Abijah was filming a home video of the father-son relationship.

"Run, run, Jack!" Abijah shouted excitedly.

The four-year-old toddler started running with a comparatively greater speed, and in a few moments, he fell on the park's green grass. Abijah and Brian rushed towards him.

"Oh, Jack!"

Brian lifted him up. The same naughty smile as his dad's was on his face.

"I am strong!" Jack said, looking at their faces.

"Oh, my God! My baby!" Abijah couldn't control her emotions.

There was an exceptional smile on Brian's face on listening to his son's words. He always motivated him whenever he fell or was hit by anything. And now Jack was repeating his words.

Brian and Abijah rushed to his side, but the mischievous little boy was already flashing a grin and proudly proclaiming his strength. Abijah couldn't help but shed tears of joy and relief at her son's resilience, while Brian beamed with pride at his son's determination...

As the night settled over London, James sat contentedly at his study table, surrounded by books, and feeling grateful for the love and support of his family. Since bringing his parents to live with him, his life has been enriched with meaning and fulfilment. Emma's illness had been successfully treated with the constant companionship of her grandparents, and both James and Olivia were able to find a balance between their personal and professional lives. Emma was blissfully happy spending time with her "nanna" and "grandpa," while James' parents were overjoyed with their son's decision.

When the clock struck eight, Olivia was busy in the kitchen, washing dishes, while Emma was tucked in bed, listening to bedtime stories from her doting grandparents. Meanwhile, James was busy tidying up his books and preparing to wind down for the night. But just as he was settling in, his mobile phone rang, interrupting the peaceful atmosphere of his home. James rose from his seat, sauntering towards the side table where his phone had been placed. Upon seeing Antonio's name light up the screen, an ear-to-ear grin spread across James' face as he eagerly answered the call and settled onto the bed. "Hello, Antonio!"

Picking up on James' excitement, Antonio tried to match it, "Hey, how are you?"

"I'm doing great, brother! And yourself?"

"I'm alright," Antonio replied, a hint of sadness in his voice.

"Is everything okay?" James asked, concerned for his parents.

"Thank God, yes, everything's fine! I'm just a bit troubled, so I thought I'd call you," Antonio explained. James' heart warmed at the thoughtfulness of his brother, "That's very kind of you. It's always a pleasure to hear from you."

"Thank you."

Antonio hesitated for a moment before finally speaking up, "James, I'm feeling terrible. I can't forgive myself."

"What's wrong, Antonio?" James asked, sensing his brother's distress.

Taking a deep breath, Antonio struggled to find the words to express his guilt, "I just... I never imagined how much pain I would cause Dad. But I can't shake off this feeling."

"Antonio, you must be kind to yourself. It wasn't your fault. Life teaches us lessons in unexpected ways," James consoled him.

"James, you have no idea what I'm going through right now. I never thought I'd hurt my father so deeply," Antonio's voice shook with emotion.

James listened intently, allowing his brother to unburden his heart.

"Mr James, I never imagined seeing him so despondent in my wildest dreams. He has abandoned all his former practices to take care of himself and his life. He's not the same person I once knew, and he's lost all his passions and the luxuries that once brought him joy. Once the fittest and most dashing person in the area, his face is now creased with wrinkles, and his once black and glossy hair is now grey. It's agonising to witness his condition," Antonio said, pausing to catch his breath. "He's not okay and informing him about my situation would only make him worse!" he said, his voice trembling.

"Why do you believe that?" James inquired.

"I've never seen him cry before, but I noticed the wetness in the corners of his eyes today. He's abandoned everything, and it pains me because it's all my fault," Antonio replied, clearing his throat. "Do you believe you're starting to love him more?" James asked immediately.

"Love! You know what, James?" Antonio took a deep breath. "I believe fathers are the most underappreciated people on earth. They make a lot of sacrifices for their families, but they are often misunderstood due to their parenting style or lack of emotional connection with their children. Regardless of how much a father loves his children or family, he does not receive the same amount of love in return. We do not love our fathers in the same way we love our mothers; instead, their personalities often appear harsh to us. And due to their strictness, children do not love them as much in most cases, not all, but some," Antonio explained, pausing again to clear his throat.

"Antonio, you're correct! You've given me a thought-provoking point to ponder. You're right; I've never seen significant celebrations on Father's Day," James said, impressed by Antonio's observation. "But even though a week has passed since Mother's

Day, the captivating city of London is still adorned with flyers and buntings. Sales and discount offers are still available in markets and shops," James continued.

Antonio's point had truly amazed him.

"I believe that the root cause behind the lack of affection towards our fathers lies in the multitude of conflicts that arise during our adolescent years. I have faced numerous challenges that have created a divide between my father and me," explained Antonio.

Curious to know more, James asked, "What sort of conflicts?"

Antonio replied, "Conflicts such as our differing communication styles, my contradictory work preferences to my father's, our opposing ideologies and political views, our distinct lifestyle choices, and his parenting methods that do not align with my beliefs of a nurturing and thoughtful father. The most difficult issue for me to deal with was the memory of him cheating on my mother with a neighbour down the street. He even took me to her house a few times. I suffered from many issues, though I was an only child. We spent less time together and never discussed any issues, such as father and son relationships, which led to a conversation gap, and despite working in the same company, we remained distant due to his lack of affection and expression. My resentment towards him increased as I grew older, further lengthening the gap in our relationship, despite sharing the same household."

Antonio paused for a moment, and his insight on fatherhood inspired James. Meanwhile, Olivia entered the room and settled in for the night. After noticing Antonio and James' conversation, she sat at the study table. She began reading a book from the shelf, Joseph Murphy's *The Power of Your Subconscious Mind*, which she was already halfway through.

After taking a deep breath, Antonio spoke calmly, "Despite the conflicts I have had with my father, and the distance in our relationship, I still yearned for his presence. When I left my home in anger and married to please my parents, I encountered a new world of difficulties. It isn't the case that I was born with a silver spoon in my mouth. I used to work in my father's company. That's why I couldn't feel the world's harshness in his presence because I was given whatever I demanded, and everything was made accessible to me. However, during those years of extreme depression and stress, I felt like I was living on another planet. My ego was at its peak, and I failed to appreciate all his efforts. Instead, I blamed him for not preparing me for the realities of this world outside his perimeter."

Antonio took another deep breath, his voice softer this time, "But now, I have come to realise that my father loves me deeply. His changed lifestyle indicates that my absence had taken away his happiness. He deserves to be loved and appreciated."

James was moved by Antonio's words and responded kindly, "Antonio, I want to thank you for sharing such a touching piece of your life with me. You should be grateful that you have come to this realisation before it is too late. God has shown you the right path, and your role as a son is more important now than ever before."

Antonio was filled with gratitude and asked, "What should I do now?"

"Listen, you have acknowledged the significance of your dad in your life. It's time to work on reducing the distance between you two. If you need any advice on how to minimise conflicts, give me some time to research, and I'll provide you with some useful information," James replied. Antonio was overwhelmed with appreciation and expressed his gratitude, "Thank you so much, James. I know how busy you are, and I'm honoured to have you in my life. I appreciate everything you have done for me, and may God continue to bless you abundantly." James responded with a gentle voice, "Antonio, please don't thank me. You are also remarkable, and I have learned so much from you. I can't explain how your presence in my life has changed my perspective. You are a great person, and you should never underestimate yourself." James inquired, "When are you scheduled to begin your chemotherapy?" Antonio replied, "I have an appointment with the doctor tomorrow and will keep you updated. Thank you so much, James!"

"You're welcome, my friend. And have you considered informing your father about your situation? He and your family will greatly support you during chemotherapy," James suggested with a caring tone.

"I plan to tell him soon, waiting for the right moment. Thank you for your concern, James. Talk to you soon," Antonio replied before ending the call.

Apologising for the interruption, James said to Olivia, "You can come here and rest now." Olivia got up from the chair and snuggled into the bed.

"How's Antonio doing?" she asked with concern.

"He's doing okay but seeing the stress his parents are going through is making him regretful," James explained.

Olivia felt a pang of sympathy for Antonio's situation.

Changing the topic, James noticed Olivia reading one of Joseph Murphy's books from his bookshelf. "That's a fantastic book! I received it from an African American gentleman named Yohan or Johan Hansen in Freetown after the war. I've searched for him everywhere, but I haven't found him. I wish I could thank him for how much this book has transformed my life and thinking process," James reminisced.

Reflecting on Antonio's story, James realised the significance of a father's love and how it impacted his childhood. He closed his eyes and pondered, rethinking his relationship with his father. James discovered an essential topic to share during the club's lecture on Saturday, further fuelling his desire to continue learning and growing. Although everything was fine in their life, he was still working to improve his family life. Someone said that the process of learning never ends; it only ends with the end of

THE FATHER AND SON RELATIONSHIP

life. So, he had learned another essential and worth-considering point on father's love through Antonio's insight that night.

Antonio stood in front of his favourite window, a serene spot from where he could witness the splendid sunrise every morning. The gentle breeze caressed his face, and he was holding a cup of tea brewed by his hands. Yet, despite the mesmerising view outside, Antonio was lost in thought and lacked his usual energy. His father, who shared Antonio's love for the beauty of the sun, had yet to wake up, and so Antonio was lost in his world of contemplation. Suddenly, Carlos appeared behind him, tapping his elbow gently, and asked how he was doing. Antonio replied that he was lost in the beauty of the sunrise. Carlos agreed that it was, as always, a sight to behold.

Then, Antonio asked his father, "Did you miss me when I left?" Carlos froze for a moment and didn't dare to meet his son's gaze. But when Antonio looked back at him, Carlos was speechless. Antonio urged him to speak his mind, "Why don't you express what you really feel and think?"

"I don't know," Carlos replied in a soft voice.

Antonio chuckled, saying, "It's because we are so similar."

How can I tell you that I badly missed you? Carlos thought. He turned on the constant staring of Antonio at his face. "What do you think?" he asked.

Antonio didn't realise that his father would ask a counter-question from him.

Antonio took a breath frowning and said, "I asked first, Dad! You always keep yourself reserved." Although Antonio mumbled the last sentence, Carlos could hear him loud and clear.

"I don't know why!" Carlos said in the same light voice.

But then Antonio remembered something important that he needed to discuss with his father. He had an appointment at the hospital that morning and needed Carlos to accompany him. Carlos looked worried, but he wasn't surprised. "I know," he whispered. "I heard your conversation with your mother a few mornings ago. I was going to talk to Bella when I heard her crying and weeping."

Antonio took a step back from his father and burst into tears. Carlos pulled him closer and hugged him tightly as if he never wanted to let go. "I am here for you, son," he said. "I am your father, I brought you into this world, and you are my only child. But if this is what God wants, we must accept it. How much time do we have left?"

"About six months," Antonio said, crying harder than before.

Carlos was overcome with emotion, and tears streamed down his face. "Let us cherish every moment we have together, my son. Let's make amends for our past and embrace the promising future ahead of us. Although the journey may be long, we will walk it together as a family, hand in hand," he said as he gently pulled his son away from his shoulder, looking deep into his eyes. "I have missed you dearly and love you more than words can express. Let's not be late for our doctor's appointment."

As the final days of April approached, James was preparing for his speech at the Youth Club. When he emerged from his room, his parents, Olivia, and Emma, were already dressed, eagerly waiting for him. After his heartfelt conversation with Antonio, James spoke to his father about their father-son relationship. His father now stood before him, beaming with gratitude and counting his many blessings in life, ready to accompany him to the Youth Club. Upon arrival, James was met with the familiar sight of a massive crowd waiting to hear him speak. His parents were amazed at the size of the audience, and the applause that erupted as James took the stage filled him with joy.

"Hello, everyone!" James exclaimed enthusiastically, his smile spreading as the audience responded with a thunderous roar. James strode confidently towards the podium, and as he reached for his laptop, he dialled Antonio's number, hoping to have him join the lecture online. However, Antonio was unavailable, and James decided to proceed with his address but recorded it for Antonio.

"I hope you're all doing well," he began excitedly. The sound of the audience's coordinated clapping echoed throughout the large hall of the Youth Club. "That's wonderful!" James exclaimed as he looked out at the audience. "As I contemplated the topic for today's lecture, God led me to one of the most significant subjects. I am deeply grateful to God and Antonio for inspiring me with this topic."

James took a deep breath, letting his eyes wander over the first row of the audience, where his loved ones were seated. His family sat beside Brian's, and he noticed Kweku sitting next to Emma, feeling grateful for his friend's support. James paused for a moment, his gaze locking onto his father, who looked back at him with a proud and encouraging smile.

"Dad! Today's topic is for you," James said, his voice ringing with warmth and love.

He continued, "Last month, London celebrated a magnificent event: Mother's Day. The city was adorned with beautiful decorations, and shopping sales continued throughout the month. Today, I want to hear from you. Ladies, hello?" James paused, eliciting chuckles from the audience. "Actually, I asked specifically for the ladies because we all know how much they love to shop," James added, a playful glint in his eyes, causing the audience to erupt in laughter. Brian playfully nudged Abijah, who turned and gave him a mock scowl.

"Please forgive my friend, Brian!" James quipped, and the laughter continued. Taking a sip of water from his bottle, James continued, "Alright, back to the topic. We all know how we celebrate Mother's Day and the grandeur with which it is commemorated. And I fully support that. Our mothers deserve all the love and appreciation in the world. But why don't we celebrate Father's Day with the same enthusiasm and splendour?"

As James spoke, a hush fell over the audience, drawn in by his words and his powerful energy. He had them under his spell.

"Why don't we celebrate Father's Day with grandiose sales that last for weeks? Why don't we bedeck our streets with delightful decor on this special day? Why do we feel hesitant to express our love to our fathers? Why does it seem like there's always an invisible distance between us and our fathers? Why can't we embrace them before starting our day like we do with our mothers? Is it not an injustice to our fathers?"

James could sense the audience's silence as they listened intently to his words. "Perhaps the young ladies present here have a close bond with their fathers, but my focus is primarily on the boys. From my observation, approximately 90% of boys lack a positive connection with their fathers. Yet, the father remains the most influential and esteemed personality in our lives, regardless of the conflicts that may arise," James explained.

"The worth of our fathers in our lives cannot be measured. No matter how much we believe we don't need our fathers, we eventually realise their significance in the later stages of life. Despite their strictness and occasionally unapproachable behaviour, we often discover that our fathers' perceptions and the sixth sense are frequently accurate."

James continued with a passionate voice, "The purpose of addressing this topic is twofold. Firstly, as parents, we must be aware of our significance in our children's lives. We must understand the incredible value we possess in our son's life. Secondly, it is time for those of you who have fathers to reconcile and let go of the past. Regardless of your father's actions, forgive them, love them, and care for them."

"The blessings of a father can make our life journey smoother through God's eyes. Their blessings provide direction and solace in times of trouble. The act of blessing one's child is both a privilege and a gift for the giver and the receiver. Fathers should pray for their children and bless them frequently, so things may go well for them and their offspring." As James concluded his heartfelt speech, the hall was filled with a serene stillness.

"Dearest Father, may you bless your beloved children regularly, particularly in this challenging era that we live in. With the chaos and hardships that we face daily, it's clear that we need each other more than ever before. So, let us take a moment to cherish and appreciate their presence in our lives. But before delving into the significance of a father's role in his son's life, allow me to express my heartfelt gratitude to you, Dad!" James spoke with admiration and gratitude as he gazed at his father.

Sitting next to Emma, his father gave him a big thumbs-up, feeling immensely blessed to have a son like James who had turned his life around.

"I sincerely desire every father and son to listen to this speech and fully grasp its message. I want you to know just how vital your role is in your son's life. As a father, you serve as a model for your child, and it's crucial that you become an excellent role model. Every aspect of your daily routine and behaviour towards family, friends, and even strangers is indelibly etched in your son's mind. Although you may not realise it, they observe and emulate your habits and traits." James paused to take a deep breath before continuing with conviction, "Your conduct and attitude towards every matter of life demonstrate to your son how to be a true man. What is a real man, you might ask? A real man is someone who inspires others, particularly his son, to be noble and virtuous. Studies and literature have repeatedly shown that a father's presence in his son's life is incredibly crucial. Children who have supportive fathers show better progress and achievement in their lives."

James took a moment to reflect before adding, "If you spend quality time with your son and listen to him, you are creating a path towards his bright future. Your presence and companionship with your son enable him to be resilient and learn from your positive attributes to remain steadfast in life's most challenging moments. In addition, your treatment of your wife and others, particularly females, influences your child's perception of how to respect and honour women, making it imperative that you lead by example."

"Every little action you do in front of your son is like a drop in the ocean, adding to his list of qualities as a man. Your son observes your every move, taking in your mannerisms, behaviours, and values. When you show up for your son and make time to listen to him, you're teaching him the importance of being present and attentive. Spending quality time with your son will nurture his character and lead him towards a brighter future. You are building a foundation for your son to stand on, and your positive presence in his life is essential for his growth and development as a person."

"However, when you're always unavailable and dismissive of your son, he'll learn that being unavailable is acceptable for a man. If you're always having tough conversations with him, he'll think that a father's role is to be harsh and unsympathetic. He'll learn that growing up alone is the norm when you're absent from his life. Unfortunately, these negative traits contribute to the high numbers of unguarded young boys on the streets getting killed and the rise of single parenting. "Simply, your actions directly impact your son's life, positively or negatively. While most fathers have a strong connection with their sons in childhood, that bond can become distanced as the son reaches adolescence and adulthood. Do you agree with me?" James paused, scanning the audience for a response. Most hands were raised in agreement.

"Now, a mother's love is different. The bond between a mother and her child is unbreakable, enduring from birth until death. It's a love that knows no bounds. But have you ever wondered what makes a mother's love so limitless?" James posed the question to the audience, and their responses were varied — love, sacrifice, support, and care.

"Yes, you all have beautifully expressed your love and admiration for your mothers. I appreciate and honour your sentiments towards your beloved mothers. However, unconditional companionship is the key ingredient that makes a mother's love boundless and everlasting." The audience gazed at James with admiration as he continued to speak, "Yes, unconditional companionship. As I have mentioned, forgiveness and friendship are the foundation of every strong and enduring relationship, and these two elements are present in a mother's love. But on the other hand, while a father's love is undoubtedly unconditional, it often appears strict and unapproachable in most cases. We all know that fathers are like the roof or shade of the house, enduring hardships first and bearing the brunt of their loved ones' anger, even though they are the most supportive ones."

The hall fell silent as everyone reflected on their fathers and their relationships with them. James then looked at his father and smiled.

"Having a father in your life is like having an impenetrable and supportive shield. Fathers are the epitome of protection, and that is precisely what they should be. The bond between a father and his son is considered the most outstanding because it's a bond of friendship and wisdom. The enduring father-son relationship benefits the son from his father's experience and decisions, which help him succeed in life. However..." James paused and surveyed the audience once more. He let out a deep sigh and continued his lecture.

"As fathers, we make mistakes. We often strive to provide our sons with a better life, but we neglect to spend time with them. We work for their future, but in doing so, we restrict their future by not being there for them. This is why we gradually lose our bond and connection with our sons." The hall was enveloped in peaceful silence, as James' point was undoubtedly true. "As fathers age, they often lose the close bond they once shared with their fathers. At the beginning, I mentioned the lack of celebration and recognition on Father's Day. It may be difficult to hear, but I want to make it clear that the reason for these unfair celebrations is none other than us."

The audience's faces were unclear as James spoke, but he continued to explain that fathers are to blame for losing their connection with their children. They become so focused on their jobs that they pay less attention to their children.

"In my next lecture, I will delve into the changes in the father-son relationship from childhood to adolescence to adulthood. I will also address the major conflicts that create distance in this relationship and provide solutions to minimise them," James concluded before receiving applause and a standing ovation.

Looking at his proud parents, James felt great joy at the sight of their priceless smiles hiding their wrinkles.

As people approached James for handshakes, Brian watched Jack with a curious but excited expression. Then, turning to his son, Brian lifted him onto his shoulders and exclaimed, "Look at this beautiful crowd!" while kissing his cheeks.

Jack's beaming smile and overflowing happiness were beyond measure. His charming face and mischievous eyes were fixed on the people meeting James.

"Do you like it?" Brian asked his son.

"Yes, Daddy! I love you!" Jack replied, surprising Brian. With his tiny and delicate hands on his father's face, Jack made his eyes even prettier and said, "Daddy, I love you!"

Abijah also noticed this sweet moment and couldn't help but smile while looking at the father-son duo. She then glanced at Mia, who was leaving the Youth Club Hall with Emma.

"It's time to go," Abijah suggested, noticing the now half-empty hall.

"We're coming," Brian replied, gazing at Jack's face with pride and love.

Perhaps it was James' heart-warming lecture or some other factor, but Brian felt an overwhelming love for Jack. As they exited the Youth Club, Jack remained perched on his father's shoulders.

"I never want to lose our bond as friends," Brian confided to James with a grin. James turned to him, his smile wide and reassuring. "You can maintain that bond. Don't forget to come to my next lecture," he said with a wink.

Brian nodded eagerly, feeling more determined than ever to be the best father he could be. As they said their goodbyes and parted ways, both families headed home with a sense of closeness and joy.

While walking towards their car, Brian reflected on James' words. He knew first-hand what it was like to have a distant relationship with a father. But he was determined to break that cycle and ensure his son didn't suffer the same fate.

"Brian, do you want me to take Jack?" Abijah asked, watching as Brian got into the driver's seat. "No, today it's me and Jack driving the car!" Brian said with a grin, hoisting his son onto his lap. Mia piped up from the back seat, "Dad, can I drive too?"

Brian chuckled. "Of course, princess. Next time we'll drive together, okay?"

Abijah watched her family with pride and gratitude, knowing how blessed they were to have found such an excellent guide in James. Together, they were committed to building a bright future for their children.

James and his family went for a refreshing morning walk with his parents the following day. Emma's health improved with all the fun activities, and his parents benefited from the exercise. As they jogged, Emma sat with her grandparents and Olivia to rest.

"It's okay, buddy. Take a breather," James called out to her from the jogging track.

"Thanks, Daddy!" Emma replied, taking a sip of juice and feeling grateful for her loving family. A smile formed on James' face as he watched Emma take a break and sip her juice. They had chosen to walk in Richmond Park, Emma's favourite park near their home. During the summer, the park was bustling with various activities and live music, making it a favourite spot for Emma and Olivia. The jogging track, lined with trees, was an invigorating addition to the park. It was the largest Royal Park in London, situated in the London Borough of Richmond upon Thames. James spotted Kweku approaching from the front as he jogged along the track. He slowed down his pace and welcomed Kweku with a smile. Kweku needed a minute to catch his breath before speaking.

"Wait for a minute," Kweku gasped.

"Take your time," James replied, smiling.

After a few seconds, Kweku expressed his admiration for James' enlightening lecture on the crucial role of fathers in their sons' lives. Kweku revealed that he never had a close bond with his father, which caused him to struggle in life. However, he observed that his friends with supportive fathers achieved remarkable success with similar goals.

James nodded his head in agreement. "Sadly, that's a common issue that many sons face."

Kweku explained that in African culture, fathers and sons don't have a close friendship-like bond, and fathers don't often share their experiences and failures with their sons, creating a gap in their relationship. This results in sons having to start from scratch to find their way. James empathetically placed his hand on Kweku's shoulder. "I understand. Some of my friends have shared similar experiences. Unfortunately, conflicts can damage the father-son relationship. I will discuss this further in our next lecture."

Kweku sighed, "But, Sir James, I think some things take a long time to change, and this is one of them. African dads can be very strict despite loving their children."

James smiled reassuringly. "Change takes time, but it's not impossible. So, let's work towards bridging that gap and creating a stronger bond between fathers and sons. Indeed, you are correct to a significant extent. Nevertheless, we must fulfil our responsibilities," James responded thoughtfully.

"Absolutely," Kweku replied.

"Alright, let's meet on Saturday at the next lecture," James suggested warmly. "Sure thing!" Kweku agreed.

After finishing their run, James approached his family, who were all joyfully entertained by Emma's tales and antics. James joined in on the laughter and quipped, "Looks like the master storyteller isn't finished yet," as he sat beside Emma.

Everyone erupted into laughter again, and the grandfather lovingly kissed Emma's head, saying, "May God protect my little angel from any harm."

Upon arriving home, James took a refreshing shower and prepared for the Youth Club. As he entered the library, he knew his upcoming lecture about fathers required extensive research and genuine information. He planned to begin by presenting his findings on the various types of conflicts that can arise in father-son relationships and then focus on the solutions to these conflicts. James found it challenging to extract the precise details he needed for his talk, but he thought of his friends who had supportive fathers and those who did not. Their experiences served as valuable insight.

"Ah, I got it!" James exclaimed to himself as he closed the books, "I should reach out to those who have unsupportive fathers and ask for their perspective on the types of conflicts." Two days later, James sat in his room surrounded by books, a pen, and a piece of paper. He gazed out the window, lost in thought. His laptop sat on the desk beside him, waiting to be used. Suddenly, the laptop rang, and Antonio appeared on the screen via Skype.

"Hey, James! Sorry for not contacting you sooner," Antonio apologised as soon as the video call began.

"Your new haircut looks great, Antonio," James complimented, admiring how it framed Antonio's face. However, he refrained from commenting on how weaker Antonio had appeared since they last met.

Antonio's eyes were filled with sadness as he spoke about the effects of chemotherapy on his physical abilities. "My hair is falling out, and it's been a struggle to eat this week," he confessed. "My parents even cut their beautiful hair to support me."

James felt a pang of sympathy for his friend. "I'm so sorry to hear that, Antonio. I wish there were something I could do to ease your pain. But please know that I'm here for you, and if you need any support, don't hesitate to ask."

Antonio's spirits lifted slightly as he responded, "There's not much we can do, but I'll stay strong and follow the process. Thank you for paying my medical bills and giving me the chance to make amends with my parents. I hope to come back to Europe soon and meet you in person. Let's stay positive and hope for the best." Antonio's enthusiasm was contagious as he eagerly asked how he could help James. "Your message said you need my help, Mr James. I'm excited to know that you need me," he said with a wide smile.

James explained that he was collecting insights and experiences about father-son relationships and was inspired by

Antonio's perspective on his relationship with his father. "What do you think about discussing this topic?" he asked.

Antonio hesitated, feeling unsure about his ability to contribute. James quickly reassured him, "Don't be shy, Antonio. Your thoughts and insights on this topic are valuable. You made me think about father-son relationships in a new light."

Despite his initial hesitation, Antonio's interest was piqued. However, he was concerned about sharing any negative experiences with James. James quickly reassured him, "Antonio, I don't want to hear anything bad about you. I'm not looking for a lecture on this topic, just your thoughts and experiences." James smiled, hoping to put Antonio's mind at ease.

James noticed a peculiar anxiety on Antonio's face, though he didn't express it in words. "Antonio, I'd love to hear your thoughts on father-son relationships and what causes the gap between fathers and sons," James said with a gentle tone. "But it's okay if you're not feeling up to it today; it's okay. You seem exhausted, and I apologise for pushing you to talk after knowing what you're going through." James looked at Antonio's face, which seemed to change colours as he spoke.

Antonio replied, "It's okay; I can talk. Your conversations help me mentally and emotionally. I just didn't understand which aspect you meant."

To ease the tension, James shared his experience with his father. "Antonio, I'm also an only son in my family. Looking at the pictures of my childhood, they show a strong bond. But when I hit adolescence, my connection with my father felt like two poles apart. This feeling continued throughout my life. Only after a very long time did I start spending time with them — mostly with my mother. Even when I was in university, it was my mother who checked on me before I cut them off. But you know what? I still don't have that kind of interaction with my dad." Antonio agreed, "You're right, James! I've had similar experiences. Whenever I criticised my father's strict behaviour towards me, my mom would show me our childhood pictures with him." James listened carefully, knowing that he had succeeded in making Antonio feel safe enough to share his experiences. "There are many reasons why fathers and sons become distant," Antonio continued. "My relationship with my father started to break down because of his strict decision-making habit. He never allowed me to make my own decisions or discuss his opinions or decisions with me. So, you know what I had to face?"

Curious, James shook his head, eager to hear more.

"I have faced numerous challenges in my life since I left the safety of my family. It was then that I discovered the workings of the real world. Prior to that, I was like a child who was spoon-fed, lacking the ability to stand on my own two feet. I was entirely dependent on my father's support. My father thought he was doing the right thing by always keeping me sheltered, but it wasn't helpful in the long run because I was unprepared for any type of job."

James attempted to connect with Antonio and said, "So, do you believe that you had to face more difficulties because your father didn't allow you to see the world as it is from the beginning?" Antonio responded, "Yes, I meant to say that my father should have discussed things with me. He should have explained the ins and outs of the business and given me a glimpse of what adulthood is like. Had he done so, I wouldn't have lost my shares, and he wouldn't have lost everything. In my opinion, if fathers share their experiences and failures with their sons, it would significantly assist them in dealing with the challenges of this world."

"Antonio, this implies that these are the factors that contribute to the distance in father-son relationships," James observed.

"I couldn't agree more," Antonio stated. "Moreover, I knew some of my friends whose fathers were supportive, yet they didn't achieve the success they deserved. When children reach adolescence, they sometimes begin to believe that their fathers are unaware of modern living techniques and that their parents are from the Stone Age. Or maybe, they are simply growing, believing that their fathers' methods of love and growth are outdated. However, let me share with you one crucial point. When they reach adulthood, they realise that their fathers were correct. James, remember that I support most fathers' financial decisions because of their experiences with failures and triumphs," Antonio added.

James pondered the conversation and asked, "Because of all these reasons, the relationship between a father and son is strained from childhood to adolescence. How do you think we can resolve these conflicts?"

"James, I believe that the little things, such as strictness and lack of openness, often create conflicts between fathers and sons over time. These conflicts arise from differences in communication styles and ways of interacting with others, as fathers and sons often have distinct approaches to socialising that can foster negativity in their bond. As we age, we naturally develop our own unique lifestyles and make different choices than our parents, whether it's due to changing times or simply because we are different individuals. These conflicts can escalate when our fathers struggle to accept our divergent paths. I myself have a different standard of living compared to my father, and we even have different sexual preferences. Despite our similarities, differences will always exist. James, do you have any suggestions for developing a better relationship with my father?" Antonio asked.

After some contemplation, Antonio suggested, "Perhaps we can reduce conflicts by accepting our fathers for who they are, personality quirks and all. It's important to remember that they have provided for us throughout our youth and continue to offer us their blessings, even if we don't always see eye to eye with them. Fathers deserve respect, love, and attention, so let's try to answer their calls and show them affection while they're still with us. Let's not wait until they're gone to celebrate their lives, as none of us can predict the future. We should make the most of our time with them now and cherish each moment."

"Absolutely spot on, James!" Antonio exclaimed, feeling inspired. "Your words are truly insightful, and I completely agree that spending quality time together is the foundation for any strong relationship. Communication and time spent together are essential, whether it's between fathers and sons, mothers and daughters, siblings, partners, or friends." He listened intently as James continued to elaborate on his ideas.

"Understanding each other is another vital aspect, and I agree that we should never dismiss our fathers' opinions just because they come from a different generation. Mutual respect is the key to building bridges and creating a solid bond."

Antonio couldn't agree more and nodded his head in agreement.

"And, of course, sharing everything with our fathers, even sensitive topics, is crucial. Being open and honest with them is the best way to strengthen our relationship. And let's not forget to celebrate even the smallest achievements and milestones together. It's a fantastic way to show our fathers we appreciate and value them."

"Absolutely marvellous points, Antonio!" exclaimed James. "It's awe-inspiring how, despite any conflicts or differences we may have with our fathers, the most important thing is to cherish and honour them. They have selflessly made countless sacrifices for us."

"Your insight is invaluable, James," replied Antonio with a warm smile. "It's been an absolute delight spending time with you!"

"It's my pleasure, Antonio," said James. "May I extend my sincerest regards to your parents? They are truly remarkable individuals. The fact that they shaved their heads in solidarity with you speaks volumes of their love and support for you."

"Thank you, Mr. James," Antonio replied humbly. "I feel incredibly fortunate to have such a great support system in my life. In times of need, we realise who truly values and loves us." "Thank you, Antonio," James said, touched. "Your presence in my life is a true blessing."

"Master James, please call my mother's cell phone if you do not hear from me next week. I am getting weaker each day, and the chemotherapy is taking a toll on me. I'm not sure if I will be able to make it, but you always encourage me to keep going and give my best. That's exactly what I am doing, but it's the worst pain and feeling ever. I am aware I only have a few weeks left, according to the doctors. So please remember me in your prayers, and if I do not make it, please remember me as Antonio — the unique and sacred bond between a father and son relationship," Antonio said calmly and tearfully.

James had tears rolling down his cheeks as he knew exactly what Antonio was relaying to him. He felt choked and lost for words. "Let's stay positive, get some rest, and I will call you next week. I love you, Antonio, and I have learnt a lot from you, thank you for being a great teacher." James dropped the call and started weeping bitterly; he could not control his emotions until Olivia came to comfort him. The feeling of losing someone is something that no one can recover from.

Chapter Nine

The Relationship Between a Mother and Her Daughter

Discuss the importance of a mother in her daughter's life.
The difference between Mom's love and Dad's love
Girls want to be like their Mom.
Discuss the relationship in childhood vs adolescence vs adulthood.

Common relationship problems between mother and daughter –
conflict during the daughter's rebellious teen years, the mother's open
communication and daughter's withdrawal, sexual proclivities,
conflict over denied needs, conflict over the son's freedom versus the
daughter's captivity, the sister-mother, the best-friend mother, the
standoffish mother.

Fixing conflicts between mother and daughter – learning to be her
Mom, not her friend, fixing the blur of lines so that each can stay on
their side of the fence, not being pushy Mom but understanding your
daughter and working at her pace, an unbiased decision that makes
daughter feel more secure in your love, find common ground,
spend quality time together, address sensitive topics –
if you don't teach her, someone else will.

Chapter Nine

The Relationship Between a Mother and Her Daughter

The cosy home is filled with the warm glow of twinkling lights and joyous laughter as night falls. Grandfather and grandmother sat together, applauding their little chef with beaming smiles. Emma, with her delicate hands, immersed herself in the dough, creating a delectable mixture for her soon-to-be chocolate cookies. The judges sitting in the front row, watching her every move, were captivated by her culinary skills and couldn't wait to taste the result. Soon, James entered the kitchen, drawn by the clapping and laughter from the living room. As he approached his daughter, he saw her mixing the dough with her long chef hat and a few strands of hair falling over her face. Excitedly, James asked, "What's going on, my little angel?"

"Daddy, I'm making chocolate cookies!" Emma replied, looking up at him with a wide smile. James leaned in and kissed her head, saying softly, "That's wonderful, my little princess!" Feeling the moment was too precious to miss, Grandpa started filming the little chef in action. "I can hardly wait to try those cookies, chef!" he exclaimed.

Emma's happiness and excitement overflowed at his words, causing her to burst out in laughter. Her slender neck bent backwards, and she covered her mouth with her hand, causing some of the mixture to stick in her mouth.

"Oops!" she exclaimed, looking down at her hand.

Everyone in the kitchen erupted in laughter once again, including Grandpa and Grandma, who were laughing heartily.

"Do I look like a joker?" Emma asked with an innocent expression on her face.

James couldn't help but burst out in laughter, spitting out a mouthful of water. Olivia, who had just finished doing laundry, entered the kitchen and couldn't hide her smile at Emma's innocent question. "Don't worry, my darling. You look like an ambitious chef," Grandma reassured Emma, pulling up a chair beside James.

"Are you feeling hungry?" she whispered to him.

"Not really," James replied.

"Okay then, your mixture is ready. Put it on the tray in different shapes," Grandma instructed, handing Emma a large tray.

"Don't forget to grease the tray with oil and butter paper," Olivia chimed in, watching over them. Seeing the opportunity to tease his daughter, James playfully said, "Emma, you can't beat your mom in cooking."

Grandpa and Grandma gave him a stern look, disapproving of his teasing.

"James, don't be jealous of my little chef," Grandpa scolded him.

"Emma, ignore him and start putting the batter on the tray," Grandma encouraged her.

"Daddy, listen to me," Emma suddenly spoke up. Everyone fell silent and turned to her. "Mom is like my cooking teacher." Olivia smiled at Emma, nodding in agreement. Emma took a deep breath and added, "We can't beat a teacher."

The unexpected reply from Emma brought an overwhelming sense of joy to Grandma and Grandpa. They beamed with pride, amazed by their granddaughter's wisdom and intelligence. James and Grandpa chuckled in their seats while Olivia watched them, her eyes sparkling with delight. Emma was the spitting image of her mother, sharing the same beauty and personality traits. She was passionate about cooking, art, and socialising, just like Olivia had been at her age. As Olivia watched Emma, memories of her childhood flooded back. She remembered when she sat by a window in a small apartment on a Caribbean Island, lost in thought as she stared at the beautiful beach and the sunrise. Her mother's gentle hand on her shoulder brought her back to the present, and she looked up to see her mother's warm smile. Olivia opened her mouth to speak, then closed it again and looked away.

"What's wrong, my dear?" her mother asked softly, sitting beside her on the sofa. Olivia and her mother had the same warm honey-coloured eyes, and as they looked at each other, Olivia couldn't help but ask, "How do you stay so happy all the time?"

Gently holding Olivia's hand, her mother spoke with a soothing tone, "I don't let the opinions of others affect me, or you, or our personal choices."

Olivia squeezed her mother's hands and said, "But mommy, the kids in my class tease me for being mixed-race and not having a dad and for being different from them."

Her mother looked at her intently and asked, "Aren't you different from them?"

Feeling sad, Olivia replied, "I don't want to be."

"Why not, my dear?" Her mother lifted her chin to meet her eyes. "You are unique, and you should be proud of that. Look at yourself, how organised you are, how good you are at studying, your personality, and your character. You have achieved so much without a father figure in your life. Embrace your individuality, and you will see that their bullying won't affect you as much." Suddenly, James' boisterous voice brought her back to the present. Emma had started shaping the batter into delicious circular cookies on the tray.

Olivia cherished her mother deeply; despite being raised by a single parent. She had been showered with love throughout her life. Yet, there were times when she yearned for a father's presence and realised its importance. But she always remained grateful and content. Likewise, for Emma, she was happy to provide all forms of love and support.

"How heart-wrenching it is for those who grow up without a mother," Olivia said, taking her mother's hand. "They miss out on having a role model in their childhood and may not experience the same quality time with their family, especially with their mother. I pray that God gives them peace and a maternal figure, although nothing can compare to a mother's love." Olivia paused to collect her thoughts and took a deep breath. James looked at her curiously and asked, "What are you thinking about, my dear?"

At first, Olivia replied, "Nothing," but seeing the doubt on James' face, she added, "I was just thinking how lucky Emma is to have such a wonderful childhood with her family." James agreed with her and said, "She is blessed indeed."

Olivia explained how important a mother's role is in a child's life, how it shapes their personality and character, and how Emma's upbringing is an excellent example. James was in awe of Olivia's wisdom and held her hand affectionately, telling her that she was the reason for Emma's happiness and development…

Meanwhile, Brian's large house was filled with joy and laughter in another part of the district. Saturday night was always a special occasion for the family, and everyone was gathered in the living room. Abijah was helping Mia with her art project while Jack and Brian painted each other's faces and tossed colours onto the floor. Jack ran after his father with his hands full of paint, enjoying the playful moment with his family.

Abijah inquired with a gentle tone, admiring their rainbow-hued faces and the myriad of paint bottles scattered across the floor, "Jack, cease this at once! You've already made quite the mess." Abijah hurried to close the open bottles' lids.

Suddenly, Jack dashed towards her and imprinted his hand on her cheek, causing him and Brian to erupt in mad laughter. Though Abijah gritted her teeth in frustration, the sight of their endearing expressions made it impossible to scold them for ruining Mia's paint. "Both father and son are peas in a pod. Look at my daughter," Abijah sat down next to Mia, "how polite and considerate she is," she remarked, delicately wiping the paint off her face. However, Jack and Brian paid no attention to her and continued to giggle uncontrollably. "Thank you, Mom!" Mia replied, prompting Abijah to feel an odd sensation. Although Mia had resumed drawing, something about her response felt unusual.

"Hush now," Brian gestured by placing his finger to his lips. "I think your mom is upset," he whispered to Jack.

"Okay, Abijah! We'll clean up the mess," Brian promised.

Abijah forced a smile, concealing her true emotions. Apart from this recent incident, their household exemplified joy, strong relationships, and excellent parenting skills. Sunday morning evoked a profound sense of tranquillity…

Emma stood at her bedroom window, basking in the birds chirping and the gentle rustling sounds that caused her hair to sway and caress her cheeks. Despite the years that had passed, her connection with nature had only grown stronger, thanks to her parents and family. Olivia emerged from the bathroom, her damp hair wrapped in a towel. She glanced at Emma, who was enjoying the morning breeze.

"Mother, would you like to go for a walk?" Emma inquired, her eyes lighting up at the sight of Olivia. "Absolutely, darling! Just let me dry my hair first," Olivia replied, gesturing towards her damp locks. Sitting beside Emma, Olivia asked, "What are you gazing at, my dear?"

"The glorious morning outside," Emma turned towards her, "I adore the delightful melody of the morning breeze!"

"Me too!" Olivia exclaimed, gazing into her daughter's sparkling eyes.

The instantaneous joy that suffused Emma's face was familiar to Olivia. Emma always blushed with happiness at any praise, and Olivia smiled as she observed her daughter's radiant cheeks. Emma was undeniably like her mother. Olivia's mother treated her the same way, bringing her immense pleasure. Running her fingers through Emma's hair, she smiled, remembering how her mother used to care for her. Without a doubt, Emma was her closest friend.

"Would you like to take a shower, my darling?" Olivia asked.

"Yes, please!" Emma replied.

"Alright, hurry up so we can go for a brisk walk," Olivia said, scooping Emma up in her arms and carrying her to the bathroom.

The weather at the park was even more pleasant. The fresh air flowed into their lungs, invigorating them. Instead of jogging on the track, James sat with his family on the grass. Holding Emma's hand, Olivia began walking on the cool grass. The bond between mother and daughter was at its pinnacle.

On the way back home, James received a call from Brian. The experiences they had shared in the past had brought them even closer. Staying in touch with high school friends after getting married is a source of happiness and a sense of accomplishment.

"Greetings, my dear friend!" James exclaimed, answering the phone with enthusiasm.

"Hello there! How are you doing?" Brian replied with equal excitement.

"I'm doing well, and yourself?"

"I'm doing fantastic, my friend!" Brian replied cheerfully.

"I've been thinking about you and your lovely family for days now," James smiled warmly as he swung open the door to his home. "Mia has been asking about Emma too."

"It's great to hear from you, Brian."

"We're actually planning a get-together tonight to celebrate Mia's recent accomplishment," Brian shared.

"What accomplishment?" James asked curiously.

"She's just passed with flying colours and was named top of her class. She also aced her group leader test. So, we want to give her a surprise," Brian explained.

James couldn't help but feel proud of Mia. "That's fantastic! Count us in."

"Great! We'll see you tonight then," Brian said with a smile.

After hanging up the phone, James called out to Emma, announcing their upcoming visit to Brian's. Emma's face lit up with excitement, and she eagerly asked, "When are we going?"

"Tonight, my love!" James replied, thrilled to see the joy in his daughter's eyes.

Emma gave him a high five as a sign of excitement, and James couldn't help but feel grateful for this moment.

Later that night, Brian beautifully decorated the lawn with twinkling lights and colourful balloons to surprise Mia. She and Jack were away at their grandparent's house so the celebration could occur without suspicion. Abijah looked around the room, checking that everything was in place for the special occasion. "Is everything ready?" she asked, smiling at Brian. "Yes, I'm just waiting for James and his family," Brian replied, reaching for his phone to call James. Abijah nodded but then had an idea. "I'll send a driver to pick up Mia and Jack from Mom's house," she said, reaching for her phone.

Brian hesitated for a moment. "Shouldn't we wait for James to arrive first?" he asked.

"They will be here on time, or let's surprise them," Abijah said with a wink.

A little while later, the car pulled up to the house and Mia and Jack stepped out. The house lights were off, making the balloons look more colourful and magical.

"Close the door, please," the driver said.

"Okay," Jack and Mia said and closed the door anxiously, looking at the darkness as the driver drove away.

They looked at each other nervously before holding hands and slowly making their way inside. The darkness made the balloons look like glowing orbs, and Mia could feel Jack's hand shaking in hers.

"It's okay, Jack. I'm here with you," Mia whispered reassuringly.

Suddenly, the lights in the house flickered on, and everyone jumped out and yelled, "Surprise!" Mia's eyes widened in shock as she entered the room filled with people and decorations. Abijah approached her daughter and said, "This is a surprise for you, Mia. You were selected as a group leader and topped your class!"

Mia was speechless. "Are you serious, Mommy?" she asked in disbelief.

Abijah nodded, tears of pride and joy filling her eyes. She hugged Mia tightly and kissed her forehead, grateful for her daughter's accomplishments.

"Yippee!" Mia squealed with excitement, almost jumping off the ground. Emma and Brian approached her with gifts, causing Mia to cover her face anxiously. Abijah looked on with pride and admiration as her daughter's smile filled the room. Jack, too, was delighted, marvelling at the colourful balloons adorning the space. Abijah had been experiencing a strange feeling since the previous day, and now, seeing Mia's unbridled excitement, she felt even more elated. Soon, it was time to cut the cake, and Mia, Emma, and Jack looked positively thrilled as they relished the festivities. Brian had even invited Abijah and James' parents to the dinner, turning the party into a beautiful example of a happy, multicultural family. The guests were all entertained by the excellent company and joyful atmosphere that filled the lawn. Both families had completed each other by providing excellent company for their guests and Mia's schoolmates.

"Abijah, I must say I am loving every moment of this fantastic party," Olivia exclaimed, sitting beside Abijah.

Abijah turned to her, beaming. "Thank you so much, dear."

"Don't thank me. You and Brian have done an incredible job today," Olivia replied, patting Abijah's shoulder.

"I never imagined Mia would enjoy her party this much. Seeing her face filled with happiness, excitement, and joy made me feel truly special. There's something about seeing your children grow happy that brings an indescribable feeling of pleasure and peace," Abijah shared her heartfelt emotions with Olivia.

"You're right. I've felt the same way about Emma for the past few days. But Abijah, I can't seem to shake this strange feeling I've had lately," Olivia said hesitantly. Noticing the change in Olivia's demeanour, Abijah gently probed, "What kind of feeling, my dear?"

"Umm! Just like you are grateful for your children, I felt the same way. Seeing Emma grow is both gleeful and scary for me. Sometimes it feels like I am giving her the best parenting, but sometimes it feels like I am missing something. When I was growing up, we didn't have such facilities, luxury-like relationships and everything I liked. So, consequently, I have to face many challenges. But for her, like other parents, I'm trying my best to keep her safe from the irony of challenges."

Abijah kept looking at her. Finally, after some seconds, she said, "It's strange that we are both thinking about the same thing." Both Abijah and Olivia couldn't control soft laughter at that.

"Mmm, I understand what you mean, Olivia. Watching our children grow brings us so much joy and a bit of fear as we want to ensure we're giving them the best possible upbringing. But unfortunately, we didn't have all the resources and support that parents have nowadays, so we had to face many challenges alone. But for our children, we'll do anything to protect them from life's hardships," Abijah replied with a warm smile.

As they both shared a soft chuckle, Olivia continued, "I truly believe that a mother is not only a child's role model but also their best friend and soul mate. Looking at the bond Emma and

I share, Abijah, I know it's a special relationship. Growing up, I had a powerful bond with my mother, which taught me so much. From a young age, I felt the purity and significance of that bond, and I never felt like I was missing anything because my mother was always there for me." Abijah listened intently to Olivia's words, grateful for their friendship and special bond. The children played joyfully in front of them while the grandparents and fathers chatted happily in their respective corners. It was a beautiful day filled with love and laughter, and Abijah couldn't help but feel a sense of contentment wash over her.

"All her hard work, late nights and sacrifices she made for me still hold a special place in my heart. And even now, I feel an unbreakable bond with my mother through the memories we shared," Olivia spoke with a wistful tone and shimmering eyes. "Watching Emma grow up reminds me of my childhood. Her habits and mannerisms reflect my personality. Seeing her develop, I realise how essential a mother's role is in her daughter's life. It breaks my heart to think that some girls may miss out on the joy and guidance that comes with having a mother in their life," she continued, pouring her heart out to Abijah.

As they shared their experiences, Olivia knew that only mothers and daughters could truly relate to the depth of her feelings. Abijah listened intently, and though she understood Olivia's situation from her perspective, she wanted to know more about her friend's childhood experiences. "What was your relationship with your mother when growing up?" Abijah asked, a touch of concern in her voice.

Olivia froze, hesitant to open up about her past. Instead, she started feeling the sweat from her body running cold and hot. Abijah's question was like someone had thrown Mount Everest on her because she had never spoken about her truth to anyone; she had kept it within her soul all these years, avoiding that question. But, again, destiny had made her stand in the court of herself, and this time, Olivia realised she needed to confront her emotions and share her story. As she struggled to find the right words, Abijah interrupted with another question, "Let me ask you something, Olivia. Do you believe that a mother and daughter can maintain a strong friendship throughout their lives?"

Olivia turned to her friend with a soft smile, relieved to answer a question that was easier to talk about. "Absolutely. I know I will always share a strong and loving bond with my mother, no matter how old I am or where life takes us," she replied.

Abijah continued the conversation and said, "But I have witnessed some of my classmates and extended friends who once had an admirable bond with their mothers, but with time, their relationship started to erode bit by bit until it completely broke down," Abijah said delicately, not wanting to touch on any personal chords for Olivia.

Olivia took a sip of her drink and replied, "Really? I have never experienced such a thing, so I am not sure about it."

"Olivia, a mother-daughter relationship is like no other, and it's truly special. I feel blessed to have such a close bond with Mia, and I know exactly what you meant earlier about feeling the purity and significance of that bond from a young age. It's a treasure we should cherish and nourish throughout our lives."

As Abijah spoke, she couldn't help but feel deep gratitude for the beautiful family she had created with Brian. They may have faced challenges in the past, but today, they are surrounded by love, happiness, and togetherness. Looking around at her loved ones, she felt her heart swell with joy.

The children's laughter filled the air, and Abijah smiled contentedly. It was moments like these that made all the hard work worth it. She raised her glass and clinked it with Olivia's.

"To motherhood," she said, her eyes sparkling with emotion.

"To motherhood," Olivia repeated, and they both took a sip of their drinks, savouring the moment. Just then, Brian and James arrived and joined their table, pulling up chairs in front of them. "How are you feeling, Olivia?" Brian asked.

"I was just telling Abijah how much I loved every moment of Mia's party. I even got the idea to have a similar one for Emma," Olivia replied, a genuine smile on her face. James and Brian chuckled at her response, and Abijah couldn't help but smile, even though something was still weighing on her mind.

The party was a success. The decorations, food, and gossip were all enjoyable, and it was clear that Mia, Emma, and Jack had a blast. The small gathering became a precious memory for all of them, and after spending time and having dinner, James suggested they leave. They left Brian's house feeling happy and satisfied.

As midnight approached, Abijah found herself lying in bed, unable to fall asleep. Though everyone else had drifted off, her thoughts and questions kept her awake.

Why don't I have cherished, heart-warming memories with my mother? the troubling thought consumed Abijah's mind. She couldn't help but wonder about her past experiences with her mother. *What is the most significant historical moment I've shared with my mother? Why can't I maintain the same connection with her in adulthood as I did in childhood? Am I a bad daughter?* Every question led to another, and her mind was racing with no end in sight. *Will Mia face the same struggles as I have? Are daughters destined to repeat the same patterns as their mothers?*

Abijah felt closer and more comfortable with her father than with her mother. She confided in him without feeling judged or jealous. He was her confidante, and he understood her better than her mother ever could. So why was it always a big deal whenever she tried to talk to her mother? Was she jealous of their relationship, or was it the other way around? Or perhaps it was her fault for leaving to explore different things after university? Her head throbbed with pain and felt like drowning in a sea of questions. For months, she had tried to improve her relationship with her mother, but nothing seemed to work. She couldn't find any answers to the endless questions swirling in her mind. Desperate for relief, Abijah got up and walked to her dressing table. She opened the drawer and retrieved a bottle of sleeping pills. She had used them before, during the tough times with Brian. And now, they were the only solution to ease her mind from the hurtful, confusing thoughts. Self-assessment was always the hardest thing, and it could leave even the most powerful men feeling defeated.

After swallowing the pill, Abijah laid back down in bed. She covered her eyes with her arm and tried to sleep in the soothing darkness, hoping to find peace from the never-ending thoughts. "Mom, Mom, wake up!" Jack's cheerful voice rang through the room, urging Abijah from her slumber. The morning sunlight had already flooded the room, filling it with a warm and inviting glow. But Abijah's head still throbbed painfully, as if she had only just gone to bed.

"Mom!" Jack's little hands shook her gently, trying to wake her up.

Abijah groaned, slowly opening her eyes. She sat up in bed, feeling the weight of exhaustion pulling her down. She made her way to the bathroom, feeling disoriented and drained. Her eyes were bloodshot when she emerged, and her complexion was ashen. Brian noticed her distress immediately.

"What's wrong, Abijah? Are you feeling, okay?" he asked, concern etched on his face.

"I'm fine," Abijah replied, trying to hide her discomfort.

Brian knew better than to push the issue, but he could tell something was weighing heavily on her. So he reached out and took her hand, hoping to offer some comfort.

"Abijah, please tell me if something is bothering you," he pleaded softly.

"It's nothing, really," Abijah said, shaking her head.

Brian knew that Abijah had been taking James' lectures for the past few months, and he wondered if they were the cause of her distress. But he didn't want to pry, knowing that Abijah valued her privacy.

As Brian left for work, Abijah was left alone with her thoughts. She felt overwhelmed by the weight of her emotions, unable to shake off the sadness that had enveloped her. She knew her relationship with her mother had always been strained, leaving a deep scar on her heart. The thought of repeating the same pattern with her daughter, Mia, filled her with dread. *Daughters are supposed to be like their mothers,* Abijah thought, feeling a lump forming in her throat. *But I don't want a broken relationship with my daughter.*

She knew she had to find a way to break the cycle of pain and hurt that had plagued her family for generations. So, she took a deep breath and resolved to take action.

"This isn't the solution," she whispered to herself, wiping away her tears. Then, finally, she got up, determined to make a change.

As Jack laid soundly in his room, Abijah sought solace in the living room, flipping through channels on the TV in hopes of finding some respite for her mind. Suddenly, a thumbnail featuring a mother and daughter caught her attention, causing her to pause and notice. She set the remote on the table, focusing intently on the program. A youthful-looking psychologist was discussing the dynamic between a mother and daughter, and Abijah's gaze remained fixed on the screen, her mind wholly engaged in the discussion. "The reality is that we all share a special bond with our mothers during our formative years. However, as time passes, that bond can become strained," the psychologist explained. Abijah absorbed the psychologist's words, feeling as though nature once again guided her in improving her relationships. But then, just as she was fully invested in the discussion, her phone rang; she refused to let it distract her from the valuable insights she was receiving. The psychologist continued, "As mothers, we tend to overlook countless factors that can eventually create distance between us and our daughters; basically, there are hundreds of factors that we ignore, and they can be the simplest of things. And in the later years, we start to feel a sudden change or gap in our relationship with our daughters. Despite how insignificant it may seem; every small detail can play a role in this distance. Moreover, it is important to acknowledge that there is a significant difference between a father's love and a mother's love." Abijah remained in rapt attention, silently contemplating how her relationship with her mother might compare. "It is also worth noting if I cannot fully describe or mention the difference between a father's love and a mother's love, as each gender, daughter and son has its own unique experiences related to the parent-child relationship," the psychologist added. "However, I will focus on the distinction between a mother's and a father's love with regard to daughters, given our limited time."

Abijah's mind swirled with thoughts as she took in the psychologist's words, grateful for the profound insights she was receiving.

As Abijah reflected on her past, memories of her mother and father flooded her mind like a warm embrace.

The scholar paused to take a breath; her words infused with a tender sweetness that only a true lover of language could possess. "If we consider the facts, every mother attests to the undeniable bond she shares with her children, especially her daughters; it might be because they share everything in common. Many studies name it a super-strong bond, born from long-term care and nurturing during pregnancy. They further declare that the pain and suffering a mother bear during birth develops an unconditional love for the child, whether it's a girl or boy. At that time, you can say that a mother's love for her daughter is intentionally greater than that of the father's, even though some might think the father-daughter relationship is closer than that of a mother-daughter relationship."

"But, over time, the love of a mother changes. These are not just my perceptions of the mother-daughter relationship. Multiple pieces of research have shown the same result. Researchers have narrated the strong relationship that develops between a girl and her father during her growing years."

As Abijah pondered her own experiences, she realised she had countless cherished memories with her father but not as many with her mother. So, after a few misunderstandings, she even started distancing herself from her mother.

The scholar continued in a gentle, soothing voice, "Let's compare the relationship between a daughter and her mother from childhood to adolescence to adulthood. As I described earlier, according to observations and studies, there is a wonderful bond between a mother and daughter in the newborn stage. However, as time passes, multiple clashes between the mother and her daughter can occur. I don't mean to say that a mother's love decreases as a girl grows older. No, a mother's love cannot be diminished for her children, whether they are daughters or sons. Rather, a mother's love revolves around nurturing her daughter, dressing her up, taking care of her cleaning, and examining her physical fitness. On the other hand, a father's love revolves around making his daughter laugh and playing with her."

Abijah was overwhelmed with empathy for her mother, realising the tremendous value of her actions, which were equally significant and vital as those of her father. As she closed her eyes, memories of her disrespectful behaviour towards her mother flooded her mind. "Our mothers are the unsung heroes of our lives, providing us with stability, health, and happiness. Sadly, daughters often fail to acknowledge and appreciate the tireless efforts of their mothers. I like to use the analogy of a tree to illustrate the love of both parents in our lives. For girls, the tree represents a girl herself. The branches and leaves represent the friends and people in her life who come and go, while the stem represents the father, providing support and encouragement and always standing by his daughter. The mother is like the roots, deeply rooted and providing life to the entire tree. She keeps the tree in its place, creates opportunities for growth and development, and has the power to make it stand strong even when cut. The roots work tirelessly behind the scenes, just like our mothers."

Abijah's eyes filled with tears as she realised how often she had pushed her mother away. "I have noticed that as girls grow older, they tend to feel a sense of distance from their mothers, often due to housework or siblings. This lack of attention leads them to become more attached to their fathers than their mothers. Adolescence is a critical stage in a girl's life, where she develops her logic, beliefs, and mindsets. It's a time of great conflict, as critical thinking and exposure to the world often clash with the restrictions and rules imposed by mothers." Abijah related to every word of this.

"During this intense energy and possessiveness phase, girls often feel that their mothers' rules and sayings are outdated and no longer relevant. This is a common reason why so many mother-daughter relationships suffer. Fathers, being open-minded, often support their daughters' freedom and happiness, which influences them to view their fathers as their buddies and their mothers as their bosses."

Abijah vividly recalled when she hurled negative words towards her mother. It was all due to a lack of understanding and distance between them.

"Based on numerous conflicts we've encountered; I believe there are at least three distinct types of mothers in our society. The first and rarest type is the best-friend mother, a mother who is like a confidante to their daughter. Just like a best friend, the mother and daughter share everything with each other, including their likes and dislikes. However, this doesn't mean that they should have the same tastes. This bond is often considered the best and worth striving for, but to our surprise, we have also witnessed numerous conflicts in such relationships." Abijah knew she had never had that kind of bond with her mother. As the scholar explained the term, Abijah couldn't help but think about having such a strong bond with her daughter Mia. However, the last lines of the scholar's words made her frown once again. "Yes, conflicts often arise in a best-friend-mother relationship, especially when a girl invites a third person, usually in the form of a boyfriend, into their life and forces the mother to agree with her. This is a common reason why such bonds are damaged."

After taking a short break, the psychologist resumed, "The second extreme type of mother is the standoffish mother. As the name suggests, children, whether boys or girls, are adversely affected by the upbringing and presence of such mothers. These mothers are often very controlling and restrictive, resulting in poor development and growth of their children."

For one more time, she thought about her mother. *No, she isn't a standoffish mother. Instead, I was the one who made her act so*, Abijah thought.

"The third type is the sister-mother. I personally love that term and those kinds of mothers. Why? Because, like sisters, they help their daughters and support them; in case of alarming signs, they fight. But the one thing that makes that relationship unique is the balance between wants and dislikes. And, that boundary, margin, limit, or whatever you say, plays its functional role in the development of a girl child."

Once again, Abijah's thoughts turned to her mother. She couldn't help but reflect on how mistaken she was in believing her mother to be distant and unapproachable. Instead, it was she who had pushed her mother away.

As she contemplated the different types of mother-daughter relationships, Abijah was drawn to the concept of a sister-mother. This unique bond was characterised by unwavering support and protection, like that of a sister, but with an added dimension of boundaries that allowed for a healthy and balanced relationship to flourish.

"Sometimes, we see the conflicts, but because of denied needs, sexual proclivities, stubbornness, mother's open communication and daughter's withdrawal, etc., we tend to ignore the conflicts and sweep them under the carpet. Many conflicts arise in a family with more than one sibling due to the son's freedom versus the daughter's captivity. But, still, there is one proven thing," the psychologist said. "No matter how offensive, hurt, and distanced you feel from your mother, as a daughter, you'll always come back to her. You will always hope for a mended relationship one day. After realising that the restrictions she made, the prohibitions she put on, the limitations she set — every single thing — were for your benefit and smooth survival and nothing else. Most probably, the time will come in every girl's life when she realises that her mother was right, and she kept a distance from her for no reason.

"Don't get me wrong, there are imperfect mothers out there, and some of them are better off kept away from your life and family because some mothers are toxic and diabolical. Some mothers just hate their children for different reasons. However, that will be a discussion for another program as we're running out of time. But before I leave, I will ask you to ponder over these simple questions; what kind of relationship do you have with your mother, and what type of mother-daughter relationships do you have with your daughter or mother? No matter where she is, tell her thank you."

Abijah's heart started racing as she felt a wave of sadness wash over her, tears streaming down her delicate cheeks, unable to control her tears and emotion. The reality of her relationship with her mother had finally hit her. As the show ended, she sat there in silence, lost in thought. Memories of her rebellious teenage years flooded her mind, and she couldn't help but feel remorseful for her past behaviour. But, looking back, she realised the unconditional love and care that her mother had always provided, despite the many conflicts they faced.

The tranquillity of nature provided her with a sense of contentment and gratitude as she reflected on the various sources of conflict that often arise between her and her mother. She only just recognised that these conflicts stemmed from a multitude of factors that she highly contributed towards. The psychologist's words provided Abijah with comfort and reassurance as she realised that deep down, no matter how hurtful or strained her relationship with her mother may be, she has always yearned for a restored connection. Eventually, she recognised the wisdom in her mother's actions, understanding that every decision was made with her well-being in mind and that every boundary set was a measure to ensure her survival and success. "Thank you," she whispered softly, grateful for this newfound awareness and the chance to build a stronger bond with her daughter, Mia, and her mother.

With a newfound determination, she quickly wiped away her tears and went to get Jack. She dressed him up and headed straight to her parent's house. As she walked in, she smiled and greeted her parents with warmth and affection. Her father engaged Jack in conversation while Abijah sat down with her mother, trying her best to remain composed. Despite her efforts, the sight of her mother proved too overwhelming, and Abijah found herself breaking down in tears. Her mother, taken aback, embraced her tightly. "Is everything okay, Abijah?" her mother asked with concern, unsure of what had caused her daughter's sudden emotional outburst. Abijah was overcome with emotion, and tears streamed down her face as she tried to lighten the heaviness in her heart. Her father was absent as he attended to Jack in another room. If he saw her in this state, he would surely worry. Her mother gently kissed her forehead, asking, "What's wrong, my dear Abijah?"

"Where's Mia?" Abijah sobbed.

"In school," her mother replied.

"And Brian's fine?" Abijah nodded.

"Then what's the matter?" Her mother tilted her head, urging her daughter to speak. "Please tell me, Abijah."

Through tears, Abijah apologised, "I'm sorry for being rude to you my whole life, for all the pain I've caused you. Please forgive me, Mother."

Her mother's eyes widened in surprise, "Oh, my dear Abijah! You don't have to say sorry. You've grown up so much, but you're still my child."

Abijah again felt like a small child, "Am I not your child?"

"Of course, you are," her mother hugged her tightly, "I forgave you a long time ago. You will always be my daughter; never forget that. Would you like me to fix your ponytail?" Abijah looked at her mother's face, surprised by the unexpected offer, and then suddenly laughed. Abijah basked in the beauty of the place, enveloped in her mother's loving embrace. The tenderness she felt within her soul that day affirmed why mothers were blessed with a divine and elevated status…

Amid her work at the restaurant, Olivia answered Abijah's call, her hands still damp from washing. "Hello, Abijah! How are you?"

"I'm doing well, Olivia! I hope you're doing well too!" Abijah replied.

"I am, thank you."

"During Mia's party, we talked about our daughter's needs and the crucial role of a mother in her life. It got me thinking for a while," Abijah explained.

"Ah, I see," Olivia said.

"I've come up with some ways that I believe are essential for cultivating the best relationship with my daughter."

"That's wonderful! I'd love to hear about it," Olivia responded.

"Thank you," Abijah beamed at the positive response. "I'll send the papers to your house so you can review them and let me know if you disagree with any point, okay?" "Sure, sure! But why don't you come over and join us for tea instead of sending it through the driver?" "I wish I could," Abijah lamented, "But Mia is having a hard time with her studies, and I need to make sure she gets back to the top of her class."

"Oh, I understand," Olivia said.

"We'll catch up soon!" Abijah promised.

"Absolutely!"

Olivia sat comfortably on the couch in her living room, still feeling the warmth of the shower she had just had. In her hands were the papers Abijah had sent her the day before, and she was eager to dive into them. The papers were of the highest quality, four A4-sized sheets beautifully printed and neatly filed. Olivia let her hair loose and opened the file, her eyes fixed on the bold title on the first page, 'Ways to have a stronger lifetime mother and daughter bond.' As she started reading, James walked in and inquired about what she was up to. She looked up at him and smiled before answering, "Abijah has sent me her findings on strengthening the bond between a mother and daughter. I'm just reading them."

"Really?" James exclaimed, impressed. "That's incredible! Do share her thoughts with me." "Of course," Olivia replied and continued reading the notes.

Abijah's words struck a chord with Olivia as she read. "To sustain a healthy and productive relationship, we must make an effort. It doesn't matter what kind of relationship we have; it's necessary to put in the work to ensure its smooth survival. The same is true for a mother-daughter relationship. As mothers, we must focus on some essential things to maintain a strong bond with our daughters for our entire lives." Olivia turned the page and continued reading, "Regardless of the type of mother-daughter relationship, be it a best friend-mother, sister-mother, or standoffish mother, we must strive to be a mother first. We must always prioritise our daughter's well-being and not let them go off and experience life freely without guidance. Our role is to be a mother and guide for them. By doing so, we can protect them from harm's way and teach them valuable life lessons."

Olivia couldn't help but nod in agreement as she finished reading the paragraph.

As Olivia took a deep breath and continued reading the notes, she couldn't help but feel grateful for their wisdom. "Here, I don't mean that you should be pushy," she read, nodding her head in agreement. "A forceful mom can't have a great relationship with her daughter." The author's words resonated with Olivia, as she knew first-hand how damaging such an approach could be. Nevertheless, she continued reading, captivated by the author's suggestion to put oneself in their daughter's shoes whenever a decision conflicted. "Actually," the author wrote, "if you think that you can treat your girl according to the rules and logic with which you grew up, you'll end up with a coldness between your daughter and yourself." Olivia couldn't agree more. She knew that her daughter was growing up in a different world, with different challenges and opportunities than the ones she had faced. It was important to let Emma live her own experiences and make her own choices. "Your daughters are meant to live according to their times, not according to yours; you have lived your life; therefore, allow them to live their own experiences. So, giving them a free space to live according to their own time will help you stay connected."

Olivia glanced at her daughter, who was sleeping peacefully on the bed. She couldn't help but smile, grateful for their beautiful bond. She knew that God had already blessed her with a wonderful daughter, and these notes were only helping her become a better mom. The author cautioned against a completely free and unguided life for children but stressed the importance of a balanced approach. "There should be a line between your relationships with your children," the author wrote, "That line indicates the respect your child has for you as a parent." Olivia nodded in agreement. "I don't believe an entirely free life is helpful for your children, especially your daughter; therefore, it is important to set some logical limitations and restrictions, but they should never blur the relationship or become a wall that hinders communication and understanding. "There should be a balance between your love, parenting and restrictions."

As the moonlight filtered through the window, illuminating the pages of the notes, Olivia felt a deep sense of peace. These words touched her heart and confirmed her instincts as a mother. She closed her eyes, grateful for this moment of reflection and wisdom.

"One of the most crucial aspects that many mothers fail to grasp is the importance of equality in their decisions. Due to familial ties, mothers may often make decisions that are heavily biased towards one child over another. As someone who has suffered from such injustices first-hand, I can attest to the damage it can cause to a mother-daughter relationship. Unfair treatment can lead to resentment and a lack of confidence in one's abilities. Sometimes, these biased decisions can take on different forms in different households. For instance, a mother's favouritism towards her sons can leave her daughters feeling left out and unimportant. That is why making time for your daughters is crucial, no matter how busy you are. Quality time spent with your daughters can lengthen your relationship, resolve conflicts and creates cherished memories that will last a lifetime. When discussing important issues with your daughter, it is essential to be open and honest. Keeping secrets and avoiding sensitive topics can lead to a breakdown in trust, which is the foundation of any strong mother-daughter relationship. It is crucial to teach your daughter how to react to difficult situations and to provide her with the tools she needs to navigate successfully through life."

Abijah's words stirred up deep emotions in Olivia, and she was grateful for the wisdom she had gained from reading her notes. Every word was a testament to the bond between a mother and her daughter. Olivia carefully closed the pages and placed them on the table before joining Emma in bed. She kissed her daughter's forehead and held her close, feeling more connected to her than ever before.

After Emma fell asleep, Olivia sat on the Chair next to the window in Emma's room. She reflected on Abijah's writing and relapsed back into her years with her mother. She started crying as she narrated one of the incidents in her thoughts.

"Your mother has travelled to your uncle's funeral; come get me some water. Take the glass." Her stepdad said.

Olivia got the water from the kitchen tap and went back into the master bedroom. "Here's your water, Dad," Olivia said.

"Come sit next to me. You've grown up into a very beautiful-looking young lady. You're prettier than your mother, and you know I love you very much." As he said those words, his hands touched Olivia unkindly, pushing her toward the bed. Olivia could not scream or fight back as she was only fourteen years old and in total shock at what was happening in her surroundings. Olivia ran away from home and went to the nearest hospital. Her stepdad was arrested and imprisoned for life, and social services took her away. She was later adopted by a lovely couple, who later turned out to be a nightmare. That was the last time she saw her mother. Tears were rolling in Olivia's eyes when she reached for her mobile phone and opened her text messages to Abijah's number. "Abijah, thank you for sharing such a wonderful piece with me. I appreciate it. You have great writing abilities, and I encourage you to write often. However, let me share with you just a few things I always wanted to share with many mothers worldwide."

"Mothers have a tremendous responsibility to guide their daughters and be role models for them. It is essential to teach our daughters how to carry themselves with grace, poise, and elegance, from dressing, talking, initiating a conversation, and knowing when to be quiet. These life skills will set them up for success and help them stand out in society. We must also teach our daughters that their self-worth is not determined by their body shape or weight but by their confidence, which is crucial in building their character from a young age. A mother must equip her daughter with life skills instead of leaving them to learn on the streets. As role models to our daughters, we must be mindful of the words we use and the company we keep around our children, particularly our daughters. We should never take our children's safety for granted and be cautious when introducing new people into their lives, especially as single mothers. It is better to err on the side of caution than to risk our children's safety.

"Sadly, some children are going astray because they lack self-awareness and do not spend enough time with their parents. With parents working long hours or neglecting their responsibilities, children may seek solace in video games and friends, which can be detrimental to their growth and development. We as mothers are responsible for protecting our children from these dangers by monitoring their online activities, knowing their whereabouts, and being aware of their friends. By doing this, we can help steer our children towards a positive path and avoid regret when they grow older. Mothers must always remain vigilant to their children's needs, listening to every word and fulfilling every need with their unwavering love and attention. While there is no perfect guidebook for motherhood, striving to be the best mother possible is a noble endeavour. Incredibles can be accomplished, and problems solved through a mother's love and heart. Above all, teaching our daughters how to love themselves and prioritise their relationship with God is crucial."

Olivia paused writing and tapped send on her phone, watching her daughter Emma sleep and contemplating their relationship and the future. Yet, one thing was certain, Olivia would go to great lengths to ensure her daughter's safety.

Suddenly, James entered the bathroom, seeing Olivia in tears and concerned for her well-being. He scooped her up into his arms, cradling her like a baby, and held her close, placing a gentle kiss on her forehead. He spoke softly, "I love you, Mrs Olivia James Tapia Kamara. I want you to consider who has caused you so much hurt that you cannot forgive them. You can choose to forgive and release yourself from their hold on your heart because when you forgive, you are doing it to set yourself free. When you forgive, you set yourself free and create a new path in your life journey. Our life journey is in our hands, and the choices we make write our story."

With a heart full of peace, James left Olivia to ponder his words and the path that lay ahead.

Chapter Ten

Bringing it Home.

A summary of what the book covered.

Chapter Ten

Bring it Home - *Summary Chapter*

$\mathcal{T}$he beauty of a relationship is truly unmatched! But to keep it flourishing, one must remember the essential elements that form the backbone of any strong bond. These key elements have been evaluated throughout this book, and they are the essence of a healthy relationship and a guide for the heart that beats with love and compassion.

The first and foremost of these keys is respect, the foundation upon which any relationship is built. Every human being is a precious creation of the Almighty, and we all deserve and crave respect. It's a beautiful feeling to be valued and cherished for who we are, just as we are. Following respect is trust, the crucial link that strengthens any relationship. It's like a magical balm that soothes any doubts or fears, a remedy for depression and anxiety. Just like when you're sitting in a car with your mother driving, and you have no idea where you're headed, but you're not scared because you trust her. The same applies to our relationship with

God. Trusting in His plans and actions means we believe our lives are in the hands of a wise, merciful, and loving being who will never disappoint us.

Last but not least, it's essential to maintain your individuality in any relationship. Whether it's with your partner, parents, or friends, striking a balance between serving others and taking care of yourself is vital.

When we allow others to dictate the direction of our lives, we tend to forget who we truly are, what we stand for, and what makes us unique. We all have our likes, dislikes, passions, and interests, and it's crucial to nurture them. After all, a fulfilling life is one that's full of happiness, excitement, and productivity.

Combining the fourth and fifth elements, we have a powerful duo that forms the foundation of any strong bond: understanding and compromising. Without understanding, it's difficult to achieve any goal or become a master of a particular skill or relationship. A deeper understanding of your purpose is necessary to reach your milestones. This is especially important in relationships where studies and research have shown that thousands of relationships end due to a lack of understanding.

When you understand your desired person, you start seeing life from their perspective. It doesn't mean you have to compromise your individuality; rather, it's about finding a balance between understanding yourself and maintaining your sense of self. This leads us to the act of compromise, which is essential in any relationship. It involves considering your partner's interests and compromising on your less significant needs to find a middle ground that benefits both parties.

Communication is vital in achieving understanding and compromise. This makes communication the sixth characteristic of a healthy relationship. Your words and actions communicate with you; without effective communication, reaching a deep understanding of the other person is impossible. So, speak from the heart, listen attentively, and express yourself clearly. Excellent problem-solving skills are the penultimate characteristic of building a good, interactive, positive relationship. This attribute can prevent conflicts and distance in relationships. The eighth characteristic, which is the primary thread in every romantic relationship, is other-centred love. Despite society's superficial interpretation of love, I firmly believe in immersing yourself in your loved one's life. It's about expanding your circle beyond your desires, needs, likes, and interests and including those of your partner. It's about acknowledging your partner's dreams, goals, actions, ideas, and thoughts. It's about prioritising your loved one's interests and goals in your life too.

All of these characteristics determine the longevity and effectiveness of a bond or relationship. The chapter on a Deeper Exploration of Good Intimate Relationships delves into maintaining a healthy and robust relationship with your partner. This chapter teaches you the true meaning of intimacy in a relationship with your partner.

According to this, sexual pleasure and other physical needs are not what makes a strong relationship. Rather, intimacy goes beyond physical contact. It involves understanding your partner, giving them space in your life, spending quality time together by finding common ground, listening to their views and interests, and creating a beautiful life together. An intimate relationship is not about losing yourself in your partner's interests and areas of influence and forgetting about your priorities. Instead, it's about expanding your life to make room for your partner. It's about pursuing your life goals, ambitions, and targets while maintaining a strong connection with your partner. This is how relationships are built - not through suppression or dominance but through mutual experiences, like the wheels of a car moving together towards the purpose of life.

We all know our roles and responsibilities in our relationships. The purpose of discussing the traits of a healthy relationship, a good partner, a supportive parent, and a loyal friend is not to judge others but to improve ourselves. It is a self-assessment tool that allows us to reflect on our roles and see if we lack any traits of a healthy relationship.

The *Ramification of a Broken Relationship* offers solutions to common relationship problems we face every day with our family, friends, and colleagues. Although fixing a broken relationship requires effort, compromises, and sometimes pain and anxiety, it is crucial for our personal growth and future sustainability.

Our environment influences us, but we also have the power to influence our surroundings. Positive and productive people inspire us to look for solutions and opportunities, while negative and ungrateful individuals can make us feel demotivated, low on confidence, or anxious. Our thoughts and behaviour impact our surroundings, and unhealthy or broken relationships have a negative effect on our personality, family, and children's mental and emotional health. Poor relationships among parents can significantly impact their children's creativity and emotional well-being.

Likewise, parents who are unable to create a strong bond with their children should be a cause for concern in the world of parenting. The ramifications of such a situation are far-reaching and extend beyond what one can imagine. The impact of unhealthy relationships is not just limited to the parents' personalities but also extends to their offspring.

These circumstances create a vast chasm between parents and their children. Children find it hard to share their emotions and feelings in an environment where parents engage in abusive and damaging relationships. It creates a feeling of detachment, making them look for solace and happiness outside the home.

There are countless examples of children who engage in criminal activities because of the fractured relationships of their parents.

In my previous chapters, "The Father and His Son" and "The Mother and Her Daughter," I discussed the same type of family conflicts. The lack of friendship between parents directly translates into a lack of connection with their children. Sons look up to their fathers, and daughters want to be like their mothers. However, children tend to distance themselves without a strong foundation of a perfect mother and father.

With time, this distance only grows, and eventually, children start drifting away from their parents. In contrast, the bonds between a father and son and a mother and daughter should be unbreakable. They should be built on a foundation of selflessness, harmony, and mutual understanding. These bonds are the epitome of natural love.

Unfortunately, many parents fail to build such a relationship with their children due to shortcomings and misunderstandings. Sons often view their fathers as stern and unyielding rather than as supportive figures. The lack of quality time spent together creates an obvious rift between fathers and their sons.

It is imperative to bridge the gaps and mend the issues present in every family with love and kindness. A father should be a supportive figure, not just for his daughters but also for his sons. Studies have demonstrated that having a friendly and supportive father can work wonders for a son. In the company of such a father, a son's chances of growth and success increase exponentially. The father's experiences and wisdom serve as a guide for his son, allowing him to achieve success more quickly than others without such a relationship.

Similarly, girls without a strong bond with their mothers suffer more than others. A mother's actions and behaviour are a model for her daughter, showing her what it means to be a woman and a mother. Our society needs to recognise that parenting is not just about basic caretaking duties like feeding and clothing children; it involves much more than that. We must acknowledge the difference between human and animal parenting.

Understanding the nature of your child is critical, and communication plays a vital role in this process. A lack of communication leads to a lack of understanding, which is a common issue in families today. Damaging family relationships among fathers, mothers, and siblings are widespread, and we must work to address these issues.

There is a solution to every problem. You can if you are determined to improve your relationships and make them more productive and fulfilling. The famous proverb, "Where there is a will, there is a way," aptly applies here. You must take the first step, no matter how difficult, to initiate change. Whether you want to improve your relationship with your spouse, partner, children, or friends, it is never too late to start.

To improve your relationship with your spouse or partner, you must acknowledge the diversity of the universe. Every being is unique, and no matter how much you love and care for your partner, they cannot be exactly like your thoughts. Accepting this diversity is crucial to building a strong, healthy relationship.

You must allow your beloved spouse or partner to bask in the joy of their interests and hobbies. Love has no rulebook that commands you to engulf your partner's entire life. Instead, it encourages you to embrace their individuality and help them grow while you also receive the same support.

As I emphasised earlier, problem-solving is the cornerstone that determines the longevity and strength of any relationship. To resolve any issues that may arise, you must step out of your comfort zone and try to understand the matter from your partner's perspective. The fundamental elements of a healthy and nurturing relationship are friendship and forgiveness. Without these, having a fulfilling and lasting bond with your partner is impossible. Accepting the diversity of the universe also means acknowledging that your partner is different from you. However, you can still maintain a deep connection by finding common ground where both of you can enjoy your lives without compromising each other's rights and desires. Forgiveness can create space in your beloved's heart, and finding ways to minimise or avoid conflicts is crucial. Communication is key here; discussing your views with your partner can help resolve the problem. But sometimes, staying connected may not be the ultimate solution, so you must learn when to hold on and let go to ensure your and your partner's well-being. Rekindling a healthy relationship is not only possible, but it is also attainable if both partners are willing to make changes. By taking the first step towards change, you begin to see the manifestation of God's assistance in your life. The bond between a husband and wife is precious and beloved in God's eyes, and by trying to improve or maintain it, you begin to feel God's special love and attention in your life.

When your decisions align with God's will, you begin to experience progress in your relationship. It is agreed that having God-centred relationships allows you to savour the beauty of life. God should be the centrepiece of every relationship, beyond everything, every goal, and every aspiration.

However, having a God-centred relationship is not about merely spending time in church, reading scriptures, isolating yourself from social life, or shunning luxury. It is about remembering Him in your every action and every doing. It means living life with Him as your master, friend, and well-wisher and trusting that He will never leave you alone in times of need. It is the faith in feeling His presence and comprehending the reasons behind His actions at different times in your life.

Having a God-centred relationship also means not forgetting our primary purpose or God while achieving worldly milestones. It means keeping in mind that our actions determine our destination, whether it be earthly or heavenly. Therefore, He should be your priority. To improve your relationships with God and others, take an introspective look and assess the quality of your relationships with the universe. Grab a pen and paper to jot down some goals; writing them down increases the chances of achieving them exponentially. Let this book leave you with positive energy and the motivation to strengthen your connections with the world and the divine.

Consider the type of relationship you aspire to improve, whether it's with God, your spouse, children, or friends. Take a moment to visualise that person and then jot down ten vital things or actions that you are committed to doing to restore a robust bond with them. Keep that piece of paper in a prominent place, such as on your study table or somewhere visible, and let your subconscious mind work on it through constant exposure. You can use this technique to enhance multiple relationships.

My goal is to encourage you to always be prepared to improve any particular relationship, leading to a joyful and satisfying life that is achievable through cultivating healthy relationships. I hope you have relished reading this book as much as I enjoyed researching and writing it. It was a life-changing experience for me, and I aspire to impact your life through its contents positively. Please share your experience with me after reading it.

I come in peace.

"The blessings of our parents can make our life journey smoother through God's eyes. Their blessings provide direction and solace in times of trouble. The act of blessing one's child is both a privilege and a gift for the giver and the receiver. Parents should pray and bless their children frequently, so things may go well for them and their offspring."

Thank you, my parents, for your countless prayers and blessings.
From your Daughter Francess Samura

I am Blessed

Francess Samura

Website: www.francesssamura.com
Email:blessed@francesssamura.com
Francess.calabash@gmail.com
Facebook: Francess Samura
Instagram: Francess.calabash